Pride and Prejudice

Adapted from Jane Austen's Novel

by

JANE KENDALL

THE DRAMATIC PUBLISHING COMPANY

Pride and Prejudice

A Romantic Comedy in Three Acts

FOR FIVE MEN AND ELEVEN WOMEN

The play was originally produced by *Robert S. Blakeslee*, and presented by *The Central Group of the Community Theatres* in cooperation with the *Chicago Park District*, May 17, 1942, at the Goodman Theatre. Costumes were designed by *Beatrice Blakeslee*. The cast was as follows:

MR. BENNET, *an easygoing man*.........Eugene R. McKeen

MRS. BENNET, *his flighty wife*............Marian Pettigrew

JANE, *their gentle daughter*...............Leana Fitzpatrick

ELIZABETH, *their independent daughter*.......Bourie Davis

MARY, *their bookish daughter*..............Marion Mueller

CATHERINE, *their fretful daughter*......Mary Grace Quinlan

LYDIA, *their flirtatious daughter*............Freda Dombek

MR. COLLINS, *a pompous young clergyman*..Edmund Anthony

MR. BINGLEY, *a friendly young man*.....Charles A. Reinhold

MISS BINGLEY, *his haughty sister*..........Loraine R. Schulz

MR. DARCY, *a proud young man*...........David Pettigrew

LADY CATHERINE DE BOURGH, *his overbearing aunt*........
.................................Dorothy Fenneman

LADY LUCAS, *a neighbor*...................Helen Burnett

CHARLOTTE, *her plain daughter*.........Dorothy Saunders

MR. WICKHAM, *a young officer*............Herbert Bakjian

HILL, *a maid*........................Michail Mooney*

*This part may be played by a man or woman.

3

PLACE: *Longbourn, the Bennet home in Hertfordshire, England.*

TIME: *About 1800.*

SYNOPSIS

NOTES ON CHARACTERS

MR. BENNET: He is a man of culture and taste, whose sense of humor has helped to carry him through some twenty-five years of marriage with his frivolous and irresponsible wife. He is handsome, with graying hair and a courteous and pleasing manner. His manner of speaking varies from dry humor to elaborate sarcasm, yet he is devoted to the real interests of his family.

MRS. BENNET: She is frivolous, irresponsible, and an inveterate matchmaker. An eligible young man has but to glance at one of her five daughters and she is ready to announce their engagement. When thwarted in any way she takes refuge in imaginary ailments and complains piteously of her "nerves." She is in her forties, with her hair elaborately done; she is always fashionably dressed. She is still pretty in a plump and florid way. It is easy to see why, twenty-five years ago, Mr. Bennet found her irresistible.

JANE: She is twenty-two, the oldest of the five daughters. Jane has always turned so beautiful and sweet a face on the world that much of it has been reflected back on her. Jane honestly believes that people are better than they are, and so is always ready to find a good excuse for any questionable act. Although docile and much under her mother's thumb, Jane is by no means lacking in spirit.

ELIZABETH: She is a beauty who also happens to have brains . . . a modern girl born in 1800! She is more like her father than any of her sisters, and, although she does not know it, she is his favorite. She is distressed at her mother's airs and obvious matchmaking, but loyally conceals it and attempts to cover her mother's blunders. She has a quick temper, a proud spirit, and is unaffected and sincere. Mr. Darcy might have resisted her beauty because of her mother's lack of taste. He cannot resist her beauty, plus the fire and spirit that are a part of Elizabeth's charm.

MARY: She is eighteen, the plain one of the family, and a bookworm. Later, Mary will probably outgrow her extreme priggishness. Right now she is prepared to lecture on practically any subject. Mary is smug and pedantic, in direct contrast to all her sisters. She is, however, likeable. You are amused rather than annoyed by her.

CATHERINE: She is seventeen, and much under the domination of her irrepressible younger sister. Catherine is slight and rather delicate in appearance. She has an engaging giggle when fun is in prospect, but, like her mother, she is inclined to whine when things do not please her.

LYDIA: She is fifteen, and utterly frivolous and irresponsible. She thinks of nothing but parties, officers, and clothes. She is not as beautiful as Jane or Elizabeth, but she is very pretty and pert, and could never, imaginably, lack a partner at a dance.

LADY LUCAS: She is in her forties, and a good friend of Mrs. Bennet, though they are rivals in matchmaking, for Lady Lucas has a daughter to marry off. Lady Lucas has a pleasant and matter-of-fact manner. In Act One she has the pleased, complacent air of one who has sighted eligible masculine quarry first.

CHARLOTTE: She is twenty-seven, and Elizabeth's special friend. Her manner is quiet and restrained and she is sweet and reasonable, though lacking somewhat in feminine charm. She does not dream of romance and is quite willing to be guided by her mother's advice.

MR. BINGLEY: He is the catch of the county, handsome, moderately rich, and with charming manners that captivate everyone who meets him. He has eyes only for Jane from the moment he sees her. He is about twenty-three.

MISS BINGLEY: She is in her twenties, and very fashionably dressed. Her surface good manners scarcely conceal her contempt for provincial society. She is proud and conceited, and her chief concern is that her brother shall make a suitable match.

MR. DARCY: He is a little older than Mr. Bingley, and a great deal richer. He is tall, handsome, and aristocratic in appearance, but his manner is cold and stiff. He is secretly just as much attracted by Elizabeth as Mr. Bingley is by Jane, but he is too intelligent not to recognize her mother's lack of taste, and so resists her as long as he can.

MR. COLLINS: He is a tall, heavy-set young clergyman, pompous and pedantic, with absurdly formal manners. Yet, he is extremely servile whenever to be so is to his advantage. He pays ridiculous court to Elizabeth, but when he fears she may not help his "career," he does not lose a moment in consoling himself elsewhere.

MR. WICKHAM: He is a handsome young officer, and cuts a dashing figure in his smart uniform. He has undeniable charm of manner, but is untrustworthy and insincere.

HILL: This part is extremely flexible. It may be played as a young servant girl in her teens or as a quiet, repressed, elderly servant. Or the part may be played as a manservant. Hill is quiet, unobtrusive, and efficient.

LADY CATHERINE: She is the dowager type, expensively dressed, formidable, and superior in manner. When she walks she sweeps; when she sits, it is as if she took her place on a throne. Quite obviously, she expects everyone to scurry at her least command. She hardly knows how to meet it when Elizabeth dares to defy her . . . but she finally sweeps regally from the room without bidding her good-bye.

CHART OF STAGE POSITIONS

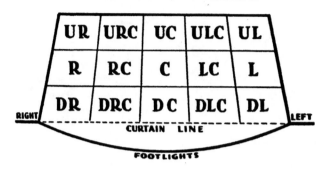

STAGE POSITIONS

Upstage means away from the footlights, *downstage* means toward the footlights, and *right* and *left* are used with reference to the actor as he faces the audience. R means *right*, L means *left*, U means *up*, D means *down*, C means *center*, and these abbreviations are used in combination, as: U R for *up right*, R C for *right center*, D L C for *down left center*, etc. One will note that a position designated on the stage refers to a general territory, rather than to a given point.

———

NOTE: Before starting rehearsals, chalk off your stage or rehearsal space as indicated above in the *Chart of Stage Positions*. Then teach your actors the meanings and positions of these fundamental terms of stage movement by having them walk from one position to another until they are familiar with them. The use of these abbreviated terms in directing the play saves time, speeds up rehearsals, and reduces the amount of explanation the director has to give to his actors.

STAGE CHART

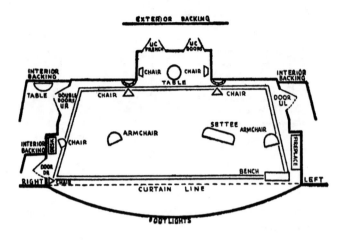

Act One

SCENE: *The living-room at Longbourn, the Bennet home. The furniture shows the effect of years of wear, but is well-chosen and attractive. There is a fireplace* D L. *Above the fireplace is a mantel on which several china figures are displayed. On the wall above the mantel is a mirror. A door* U L *leads to the library, Mr. Bennet's favorite retreat. Two sets of long glass doors are set off in an alcove* U C *and open upon a graveled walk, revealing a glimpse of shrubbery and a flower garden. Double doors* U R *lead to the front hall. There is a door* D R *which leads to the back part of the house. Above this door is a writing desk and a chair. Below the door is a straight chair. There is an armchair at* R C, *and a small settee at* L C. *Downstage of the fireplace, at a right angle to it, is a backless bench. There is another armchair above this bench, half facing the fireplace. Straight chairs are against the wall on either side of the alcove* U C. *In the center of the alcove is a small round table. Two rather massive, highly-carved chairs face each other from either side of the walls in the alcove* U C. *The furniture is English, of the period about 1800. Family portraits hang on the walls. This is the home of a family who, although they are well-to-do but not wealthy, live according to the standards of the English gentry.* NOTE: *To simplify the setting, it is suggested that the alcove* U C *be eliminated. Merely use one set of glass doors opening out into the garden. The table* U C, *the only piece of furniture in the alcove actually used, may be set to one side of the doors* U C.]

AT RISE OF CURTAIN: *It is a sunny afternoon in late March.*

Although this is a spring month, the air is still quite chill, and there is a fire burning in the fireplace. MR. BENNET *sits in the armchair near it, with a book, smoking his pipe. He is a man in his forties, whose sense of humor has helped to carry him through twenty-five years of marriage with his frivolous and irresponsible wife.* MARY *is seated at the writing desk at* R *stage, copying extracts from a ponderous volume into a copybook. On the desk before her are quill pens and ink.* MARY, *who is eighteen, is the plain one of the family. She is smug and pedantic, in direct contrast to her other sisters. She is, however, likeable. You are amused rather than annoyed by her. When* MARY *speaks, it is usually to utter, in a smug voice, platitudes, which she considers gems of wisdom.* JANE, *twenty-two, is the oldest and the most beautiful daughter. She is sitting in the armchair at* R C, *doing a piece of fine embroidery. Her natural sweetness and gentleness lead her to think the best of everyone.* LYDIA, *the youngest, is standing left of the table* U C, *engaged in snipping the trimming from a new bonnet. The gayly-colored bandbox it came in lies on the table.* LYDIA *is fifteen, and utterly frivolous and irresponsible. She thinks of nothing but parties, clothes, and officers. She is not as beautiful as* JANE *or* ELIZABETH, *but she is very pretty and pert.* CATHERINE, *who is seventeen, is standing right of the table. She is a slight, rather delicate girl, who is completely under the domination of her younger sister. She giggles a great deal when happy, but is fretful and peevish if things go wrong. As the curtain rises,* CATHERINE *and* LYDIA *run lightly downstage to in front of the settee, giggling.* LYDIA *tries on the bonnet and glances at herself in the mirror over the fireplace.* CATHERINE *stands right of her, admiring the effect.*]

LYDIA [*holding up a piece of satin trimming which dangles from the bonnet*]. Hold this piece while I snip it off, Kitty.

[*The two girls hurry back to the table* U C, *giggling. Obediently,* CATHERINE *holds the piece of trimming, and* LYDIA *snips.*]

JANE [*looking up from her embroidering*]. Why did you buy the bonnet, Lydia, if you don't think it pretty?

LYDIA [*airily*]. La! I thought I might as well buy it as not. I shall pull it to pieces and see if I can make it up any better.

CATHERINE. There were two or three much uglier in the shop.

MARY [*turning from her writing*]. One of my most sensible extracts says that beauty is often in the eye of the beholder. I consider it a thought worth pondering.

CATHERINE [*lightly*]. When Lydia and I prefer pondering to enjoying ourselves, Mary, we will think about it.

[CATHERINE *and* LYDIA *giggle and move* D L C *again.* LYDIA *tries on the bonnet as before.* MARY *returns to her writing, slightly put out by* CATHERINE'S *flip reply.*]

LYDIA [*glancing toward the mirror*]. I think it will be very tolerable when I trim it with some prettier-colored satin.

[MR. BENNET *coughs, annoyed by the chatter, and shifts his position in his chair.* LYDIA *shushes* CATHERINE, *who is giggling, and they both return on tiptoe to* U C.]

JANE. I think you just wanted another bandbox.

LYDIA. La! What if I did? [*She tosses her head and continues to snip.*]

[MRS. BENNET *hurries in* U R. *She is a pretty woman in her early forties, frivolous and irresponsible, and an inveterate matchmaker. An eligible young man has but to glance at one of her five daughters and she is ready to announce their engagement. She is forever complaining of imaginary ailments and her "nerves." At the moment, she is somewhat excited.*]

MRS. BENNET [*advancing on* MR. BENNET, *above the settee, to right of his chair*]. My dear Mr. Bennet, have you heard the news? Netherfield Park is let at last!

MR. BENNET [*showing little interest, not looking up from his book*]. Is it? [*He continues to read.*]

MRS. BENNET. Mrs. Long has just been here and told me all about it.

[MR. BENNET *makes no answer but a negative grunt.* MRS. BENNET *pauses expectantly.*]

MRS. BENNET [*impatiently*]. Don't you want to know who has taken it?

MR. BENNET [*looking up with a sigh*]. *You* want to tell me, and *I* have no objection to hearing it.

MRS. BENNET [*eagerly*]. A young man of *great fortune* from the north of England.

JANE. What's his name?

MRS. BENNET. Bingley.

[LYDIA *has finished snipping off the trimming from the bonnet and tries it on. She now takes a hand mirror from the table and admires herself.*]

MR. BENNET. Is he married or single?

MRS. BENNET. Oh, single, my dear, to be sure! A single man of large fortune—four or five thousand pounds a year. [*She looks about at the girls.*] What a fine thing for our girls!

LYDIA [*posing before the hand mirror*]. Oh, Kitty and I have already heard your news from Aunt Phillips at Meryton.

CATHERINE. A man must wear a uniform, or we can't see him at all. [*She giggles.*]

MRS. BENNET [*reminiscently*]. I remember the time when I liked a red coat myself. [*She crosses* U C, *takes the mirror from* LYDIA, *and preens.*]

MR. BENNET. At heart you still do, my dear.

MRS. BENNET. If a smart young colonel, with five or six thousand a year, should want one of my girls, I shall not say nay to him.

JANE. Lydia considers Mr. Wickham the most elegant of the officers at Meryton. [*She adds teasingly.*] Though I doubt if he has a private fortune.

LYDIA. Do you think I'd *ask* him about a thing like that?

[CATHERINE *giggles.* LYDIA *takes off the bonnet.*]

LYDIA. Anyway, he has his eye on my sister Elizabeth. [*She begins to gather up her things.*]

CATHERINE [*helping her*]. Are you going to finish it upstairs?

LYDIA. Yes. [*She crosses* U R.] Bring the satin with you.

[LYDIA *goes out* U R, *followed by* CATHERINE, *who brings the rest of the trimmings and the bandbox.*]

MRS. BENNET [*moving toward* MARY]. Mary, my dear. What I have to discuss with your father will be of more interest to your elder sisters.

MARY. Then I shall retire to my room for a little further study. [*She picks up the book and starts* U R.]

[MARY *goes out* U R. MRS. BENNET *moves to right of* JANE.]

MR. BENNET. Now, my dear, how does Mr. Bingley's fortune concern Jane and Elizabeth?

MRS. BENNET. My dear Mr. Bennet, how can you be so tiresome! You know that I am thinking of his marrying one of them.

JANE [*protesting*]. But, Mama,* we have not even met the gentleman!

MRS. BENNET [*as if it were a foregone conclusion*]. It is very likely that Mr. Bingley may fall in love with one of you.

MR. BENNET [*dryly*]. Is that his reason for settling here?

MRS. BENNET [*ignoring this remark, crossing to him*]. You must visit him at once.

MR. BENNET. You and the girls may go. You are as handsome as any of them, and Mr. Bingley might like you the best of the party.

MRS. BENNET [*her anger momentarily forgotten, pleased*]. My dear, you flatter me. [*She crosses to left of the table* U C, *takes up the mirror again, and fusses with her hair.*] I certainly *have* had my share of beauty, but I don't pretend to be extraordinary, now that I have five grown-up daughters. [*She replaces the mirror and moves down to behind the settee.*]

[ELIZABETH *comes in* U R. *She is a beauty who also happens to have brains . . . a modern girl born in 1800. She has a quick temper, a proud spirit, and is unaffected and sincere. She has evidently been walking, for her hair is a little blown and she wears an outdoor wrap.*]

ELIZABETH. What a fine walk I've had! [*She goes down to left of* JANE.] Oh, Jane, you should have come with me!

MRS. BENNET. She had her needlework to finish.

JANE. Elizabeth, Mama has just been telling us that Netherfield is let.

ELIZABETH [*crossing to the bench by the fireplace and sitting*]. So Charlotte Lucas told me this morning. [*She warms her hands.*]

---

*Pronounced "Ma-ma'" and "Pa-pa'," with the accent on the last syllable.

MRS. BENNET [*reproachfully, moving to* C *stage*]. And you didn't confide in your own mother!

ELIZABETH. Sir William Lucas and Lady Lucas have already called on Mr. Bingley. Charlotte says he has very pleasing manners.

MRS. BENNET [*crossing over to* MR. BENNET]. Do you hear that, Mr. Bennet? Please consider your daughters. It will be impossible for us to visit him if you do not.

MR. BENNET. I dare say Mr. Bingley will be very glad to see you. I'll send a few lines by you to assure him of my hearty consent to his marrying whichever he chooses of my daughters.

ELIZABETH [*shaking her finger at him*]. Now, Papa! [*She takes off her wrap as she moves to* JANE.] Will you come with me to my room, Jane? [*She speaks teasingly.*] Mama may feel she can talk more freely in our absence.

[ELIZABETH *starts* U R, *and* JANE *follows.*]

MRS. BENNET. Order tea served in a few minutes, Lizzy.

ELIZABETH. Yes, Mama.

[ELIZABETH *and* JANE *go out* U R. MRS. BENNET *turns with new determination to* MR. BENNET, *who has tried to continue his reading.*]

MRS. BENNET. Mr. Bennet, I insist that you call on Mr. Bingley immediately. Only think what an establishment it will be for one of your daughters!

MR. BENNET. H'm? [*He looks up.*] Then I must throw in a good word for my little Lizzy.

MRS. BENNET [*huffily, moving a step toward* C *stage*]. You will do no such thing! Lizzy is not a bit better than the others, and I'm sure she is not half so handsome as Jane, nor half so good-humored as Lydia.

MR. BENNET. No?

MRS. BENNET. But you are always giving *her* the preference.

MR. BENNET. Am I?

MRS. BENNET. You take delight in vexing me. [*With a plaintive sigh, she sits on the settee.*] You have no consideration for my poor nerves. [*She dabs at her eyes with her handkerchief.*]

MR. BENNET. You mistake me, my dear. I have a high respect for your nerves. They are my old friends. I have heard you mention them with consideration these twenty years.

MRS. BENNET [*her voice choked with sobs*]. Ah! You don't know what I suffer!

MR. BENNET [*rising, moving to the settee*]. But you will get over it, and live to see many young men of four thousand a year come into the neighborhood. [*He goes* U L.] I hope to be undisturbed in the library.

[MR. BENNET *goes out* U L. MRS. BENNET *continues to dab at her eyes. Then she sighs, and rises as* HILL, *a maid, enters* U R. HILL *is an attractive young girl in her teens. If desired, this part may be played by an older woman, or a man.*]

HILL [*coming to* C]. Lady Lucas and Miss Charlotte Lucas, madam.

MRS. BENNET [*moving to* C]. Show them in. And, Hill, tell Miss Jane and Miss Elizabeth that we have guests.

HILL. Yes, madam.

[HILL *curtsies and goes out* U R. MRS. BENNET *moves toward the fireplace, dabs at her eyes once more, and turns as* HILL *re-enters* U R *with* LADY LUCAS *and* CHARLOTTE. HILL *then goes out* U R. LADY LUCAS *is in her forties, and a good friend of* MRS. BENNET, *though they are rivals in matchmaking. She has the pleased, complacent air of one who has sighted the eligible masculine quarry first.* CHARLOTTE, *who is twenty-seven, is quiet and restrained, though lacking somewhat in feminine charm. She and* ELIZABETH *are close friends.*]

MRS. BENNET [*moving to* C *to meet them, effusively*]. Good afternoon, Lady Lucas. [*She kisses her on the cheek.*] And Charlotte, my dear. How well you are looking!

LADY LUCAS. We have but a short time to stay.

MRS. BENNET [*ushering* LADY LUCAS *to the settee*]. Don't say that—when I have been looking forward to a nice long chat!

LADY LUCAS [*sitting on the settee*]. I thought you would be interested to know that we have called at Netherfield, and our call has been returned. [*She speaks smugly.*]

[CHARLOTTE *sits primly in the armchair at* R C. HILL *comes in* U R *and pauses respectfully at the door.*]

MRS. BENNET [*sitting beside* LADY LUCAS]. So soon! How agreeable of him! [*She is disturbed by this news.*]

CHARLOTTE. I had hoped to see Elizabeth.

HILL. Miss Jane and Miss Elizabeth are coming downstairs.

[HILL *goes out* U R *as* JANE *and* ELIZABETH *come in* U R. JANE *carries her embroidery with her.*]

ELIZABETH [*going to* C *and curtseying*]. Good day, Lady Lucas. [*She crosses to* CHARLOTTE *and kisses her.*] Charlotte! I'm glad you came over.

CHARLOTTE. And I.

JANE [*following* ELIZABETH, *curtseying at* C]. How nice to see you, Lady Lucas. [*She crosses to* CHARLOTTE *and kisses her.*]

LADY LUCAS. We are on our way to make other calls, my dear. Has Charlotte told you she has met Mr. Bingley? [*She beams proudly.*]

[MRS. BENNET *glances at her daughters with an "I told you so" expression.* JANE *moves* D L *and sits on the bench by the fireplace, while* ELIZABETH *sits in the chair by the desk at* R *stage.*]

ELIZABETH [*on the spoken cue, "—met Mr. Bingley?"*]. Yes, and that he asked her for the honor of the first dance when he gives his ball at Netherfield.

JANE [*sincerely*]. How nice for you, Charlotte!

CHARLOTTE. It is only a gesture of politeness. He has not yet seen you, Jane.

MRS. BENNET. I am distressed that Mr. Bennet has not called upon Mr. Bingley. A most pleasing young man, I hear.

LADY LUCAS. Very agreeable. His sister, Miss Bingley, who is to keep house for him, is a very fine lady—used to London society.

CHARLOTTE. It will be pleasant to have her in the neighborhood. He has a friend visiting him, too. A Mr. Darcy.

MRS. BENNET [*interested*]. Oh—*another* young man?

LADY LUCAS. Reported to have an income of ten thousand pounds a year.

MRS. BENNET [*extremely impressed*]. Ten thousand pounds!

CHARLOTTE. I thought him handsome, but with proud and disagreeable manners.

MRS. BENNET [*distressed*]. *Why* doesn't Mr. Bennet call! [*She twists her handkerchief nervously.*]

JANE. Do not distress yourself, Mama. No doubt we shall meet him at the assemblies.

MRS. BENNET [*with determination*]. I *must* prevail on Mr. Bennet to call upon Mr. Bingley at once.

LADY LUCAS [*politely*]. Indeed, you must. [*She rises.*] Come, Charlotte, we must be on our way.

[CHARLOTTE *rises. The others rise.*]

CHARLOTTE [*to* ELIZABETH]. Perhaps we can have another of our walks tomorrow morning.

ELIZABETH. I shall be looking forward to it.

LADY LUCAS [*moving to* C]. It's been a delightful chat! Good afternoon, ladies.

[LADY LUCAS *and* CHARLOTTE *go out* U R, *amidst a chattering of* "*good-byes.*"]

MRS. BENNET [*moving* U R C]. Dear me, I am so upset by your father's conduct! Charlotte Lucas may have a husband before any of you.

JANE [*crossing to the armchair* R C, *sitting, and continuing her embroidery work*]. Charlotte is our very good friend, and we wish her well.

MRS. BENNET [*coming down to behind the armchair* R C]. Lady Lucas is a selfish, designing woman, and called but to gloat over me. I can see plainly that she schemes to marry Charlotte to Mr. Bingley.

ELIZABETH [*crossing* D L *and sitting on the bench, with a book which she takes from the desk*]. Nonsense, Mama! Charlotte has a mind of her own, and so, no doubt, has the young man. [*She tries to read.*]

MRS. BENNET. How can your father upset my poor nerves like this! [*She walks about agitatedly, to* U C *and down to* C.]

[MR. BENNET *comes in* U L. *He has a letter in his hand.*]

MR. BENNET [*pausing back of the armchair at* L *stage*]. I hope, my dear, that you have ordered a good dinner for today. I have reason to expect an addition to our family party.

MRS. BENNET [*pausing at* C *stage*]. Who do you mean? [*She moves to the settee.*] Unless—Elizabeth, did you invite Charlotte Lucas?

ELIZABETH. No, Mama.

MR. BENNET. The person of whom I speak is a gentleman, and a stranger.

MRS. BENNET [*her face lighting up*]. It *is* Mr. Bingley, I'm sure! You did call on him! [*She sits on the settee.*] How unlucky—there is not a bit of fish to be got today. [*She is all aflutter.*] Jane, my love, summon Hill this moment.

MR. BENNET. It is *not* Mr. Bingley. It is a person whom I never saw before in my life.

ELIZABETH. If you never saw him before, how do you know he's coming?

MRS. BENNET. Your father speaks in riddles purposely to vex my poor nerves.

MR. BENNET [*moving behind the settee to* C *stage*]. You will observe, my dear, that I have a letter. [*He holds it up.*]

MRS. BENNET [*reproachfully*]. *I* didn't know that you had a letter.

MR. BENNET. You gave me no chance to mention it earlier. It came a fortnight ago, and I have already answered it. It is from my cousin, Mr. Collins.

MRS. BENNET [*with a shudder*]. Pray, do not talk of that odious man! Mr. Collins—indeed! Can't he wait until you're dead to turn us all out of this house? [*She starts to weep.*]

MR. BENNET [*patiently, having explained this many times before, but to no avail*]. My dear, nothing we can do will keep Mr. Collins from inheriting Longbourn when I die.

MRS. BENNET. I do think it is the hardest thing in the world that your estate should be entailed away from your own children. [*She dabs at her eyes.*]

JANE. It is the law, Mama.

MRS. BENNET [*with a wail*]. I cannot bear to think of it.

MR. BENNET. But when you hear what he has to say, you may be a little softened toward him.

MRS. BENNET. I am sure I shall not. I think it was very impertinent of him to write to you at all.

MR. BENNET. For one thing, he says that he has received his ordination.

ELIZABETH. Oh, a clergyman!

MR. BENNET. And that he has been appointed to a rectory by the patronage of the Lady Catherine de Bourgh.

ELIZABETH [*unimpressed*]. Whoever she may be.

MR. BENNET. At any rate, he is coming here today for a fortnight's visit.

MRS. BENNET [*coldly*]. Am I supposed to make him welcome?

MR. BENNET. Judge for yourself by this line. [*He reads from the letter.*] "I cannot be otherwise than concerned at being the means of injuring your amiable daughters——"

MRS. BENNET. I am glad he realizes it.

MR. BENNET. "——and beg leave to apologize for it, as well as to assure you of my readiness to make them every possible amends."

MRS. BENNET [*more heartened*]. If he is disposed to make any amends, *I* shall not be the person to discourage him.

MR. BENNET. I am impatient to see him.

MRS. BENNET. *I* am impatient to see Mr. Bingley. Why do you remain so stubborn in this matter?

MR. BENNET [*crossing to right of the settee*]. If it will relieve your poor nerves, my dear, I have already called on the young gentleman.

JANE. Oh, Papa, you *have?*

MRS. BENNET [*overjoyed, rising*]. How good of you!

MR. BENNET [*dryly*]. Thank you, my dear. [*He moves above the settee to the fireplace.*]

ELIZABETH [*laughing*]. This is Papa's idea of a good joke on us all.

JANE. To call and never say a word about it till now! [*She laughs.*]

ELIZABETH. And let Mama tell *him* all about Mr. Bingley!

MRS. BENNET [*in good humor again*]. Lady Lucas will soon see that Charlotte is no whit ahead of my own girls!

[LYDIA *and* CATHERINE *hurry in* U R.]

LYDIA [*loudly, racing over to right of the settee*]. Mama, what do you think?

CATHERINE [*following* LYDIA]. We saw it from our window upstairs!

MR. BENNET. What are they talking about?

[*But* LYDIA *and* CATHERINE *dash to the French windows* U C *to peek out excitedly.*]

LYDIA. The carriage from Netherfield!

CATHERINE. It is stopping out front!

LYDIA. A young gentleman is getting out. It must be Mr. Bingley.

CATHERINE. He has a fine blue coat.

LYDIA. A lady is with him, and another gentleman.

MRS. BENNET [*excitedly*]. Elizabeth, smooth down your hair!

ELIZABETH. Yes, Mama. [*She does so.*]

[HILL *comes in* U R *and pauses there.*]

HILL. Mr. Bingley, Miss Bingley, and Mr. Darcy.

MR. BENNET. Show them in.

HILL. Yes, sir. [*She starts out.*]

MRS. BENNET [*calling after her*]. Then bring the tea in at once.

HILL [*pausing*]. Yes, madam.

MRS. BENNET. And tell Miss Mary to come down immediately.

HILL. Yes, madam.

[HILL *goes out* U R. LYDIA *and* CATHERINE *come down to* C *stage.*]

MRS. BENNET [*flustered*]. Mary makes such a good impression on visitors. She is so very intelligent. Jane, my dear, be composed, as I am. We must not show undue interest.

JANE [*demurely*]. Yes, Mama.

MRS. BENNET. Lydia and Kitty, remember your manners, and tone down your voices.

[LYDIA *and* CATHERINE, *who have been prinking, take seats.* LYDIA *sits in the chair by the desk, while* CATHERINE *sits in the chair below the door* D R.]

MRS. BENNET. Resume your needlework, Jane. Men admire an accomplished young woman.

[*Obediently,* JANE *takes up her embroidery.*]

MRS. BENNET. Elizabeth, watch your sharp tongue. [*She sits on the settee.*]

ELIZABETH [*meekly, with a side glance at* MR. BENNET]. Yes, Mama.

[*There is considerable flurry as* MRS. BENNET *and the girls get settled, straightening their dresses and fixing their hair. At last, all is quiet and composed.*]

MR. BENNET [*moving above the settee to* U C, *glancing about at the group*]. My dear, I think for the moment your family is under control.

[HILL *re-enters* U R *with the visitors.* MR. CHARLES BINGLEY *is about twenty-three, the catch of the county, handsome, moderately rich, and with charming manners that captivate everyone who meets him.* MISS CAROLINE BINGLEY *is in her twenties, and very fashionably dressed. Her surface good manners scarcely conceal her contempt for provincial society. She is proud and conceited, and her chief concern is that her brother shall make a suitable match.* MR. FITZWILLIAM DARCY *is a little older than* MR. BINGLEY, *and a great deal richer. He is tall, handsome, and aristocratic in appearance, but his manner is cold and stiff. While* MR. BINGLEY *finds it easy to make friends,* MR. DARCY *finds it difficult. As they enter, the ladies rise. The guests cross to* MR. BENNET.]

MR. BENNET. Good afternoon. May I present my wife and daughters, Miss Jane, Miss Elizabeth, Miss Catherine, and Miss Lydia?

[HILL *goes out* D R. *With one low sweeping bow,* MR. BINGLEY *greets the ladies, and the ladies curtsey.*]

MR. BINGLEY. It is a great pleasure. Let me present my sister, Miss Bingley, who has desired to make your acquaintance.

MRS. BENNET [*gushing*]. How delighted I am, my dear Miss Bingley!

MISS BINGLEY. And my friend, Mr. Darcy.

[MR. DARCY *bows coldly. His aloof manner is a sharp contrast to the friendliness of* MR. BINGLEY. *The ladies curtsey to him, but the sweep of their curtseys is somewhat shortened by* MR. DARCY'S *coolness.*]

MRS. BENNET [*fluttering and over-cordial*]. Pray be seated. We shall have tea in a moment.

[MISS BINGLEY *sits on the settee.* MRS. BENNET *sits next to her.* LYDIA *and* CATHERINE *resume their seats, as do* JANE *and* ELIZABETH. MR. BINGLEY *moves toward* JANE *and stands right of her chair, greatly attracted to her.* MR. DARCY *moves behind the settee, to the fireplace, and stands in front of it, stiffly.* MR. BENNET *remains standing by the up right corner of the settee.*]

MR. BENNET. I hope you are well established at Netherfield by now.

MR. BINGLEY. Yes, indeed, thanks to the excellent management of my sister. I am looking forward to a pleasant stay.

MRS. BENNET. I don't know a place in the county that is the equal of Netherfield. You will not think of quitting in a hurry, I hope?

MISS BINGLEY. Whatever my brother does is done in a hurry.

MR. BINGLEY. If I should resolve to quit Netherfield, I should probably be off in five minutes. At present, however, I find the surroundings quite charming. [*He glances at* JANE, *who lowers her head.*]

MR. DARCY [*stiffly*]. I can't abide the country. One moves in such limited society.

ELIZABETH [*defensively*]. But people themselves alter so much, that there is something new to be observed in them forever.

[MR. DARCY *looks at her, but does not reply.* HILL *comes in* D R. *She carries a tea table with tea service and a plate of tiny sandwiches. She sets it just to the right of* MRS. BENNET *and goes out* U R. MRS. BENNET *pours the tea as they continue their conversation, and* JANE *passes it to the guests and the family.* MR. BINGLEY *watches* JANE *intently. When she serves him a sandwich, he takes a long time to select his, because he looks at* JANE *instead.*]

MRS. BENNET. I can't see that London has a great advantage over the country, except for the shops. The country is a great deal pleasanter, is it not, Mr. Bingley?

MR. BINGLEY. When I am in the country, I never wish to leave it.

MISS BINGLEY. And when he is in town, it is pretty much the same.

MR. BINGLEY. I can be equally happy in either.

MRS. BENNET. That is because you have the right disposition. But this gentleman—[*She looks at* MR. DARCY.]—seems to think the country is nothing at all.

JANE [*ill at ease for her mother*]. Indeed, Mama, you quite mistook Mr. Darcy. He only meant that there was not such a variety of people to be met with in the country as in town.

MRS. BENNET [*proudly and affectedly*]. I know *we* dine with four-and-twenty families!

[MISS BINGLEY *exchanges amused glances with* MR. DARCY. ELIZABETH *notices this, and is embarrassed for her mother.*]

LYDIA [*loudly*]. Did you know the officers are stationed at Meryton, Mr. Bingley? La! What fun we have with them!

[LYDIA *and* CATHERINE *giggle.* MISS BINGLEY *raises her eyebrows and looks at* MR. DARCY.]

MRS. BENNET. You know how young girls fancy a red coat. I was once that way myself.

MISS BINGLEY [*slightly shocked*]. Indeed!

ELIZABETH [*quickly, to* MR. BINGLEY]. I understand you have met Miss Lucas.

MR. BINGLEY. Yes, I have called upon the family.

JANE. Charlotte is our dear friend.

MRS. BENNET. What an agreeable man Sir William is! So much the man of fashion—so genteel, so easy.

MR. BINGLEY. He certainly is.

MRS. BENNET. He has always something to say to everybody. *That* is my idea of good breeding, and those persons who fancy themselves very important, and never open their mouths, quite mistake the matter. [*She looks pointedly at* MR. DARCY.]

ELIZABETH [*hastily*]. Charlotte was here this afternoon. You just missed seeing her.

MRS. BENNET. A very good sort of girl. What a pity she is not handsome! Not that *I* think Charlotte is so *very* plain.

MR. BINGLEY. She seems a very pleasant young woman.

MRS. BENNET. Oh, dear, yes—but you must own she is very plain.

[LYDIA *and* CATHERINE *giggle at this.*]

MR. BENNET. Surely, my dear, you can find some subject of more interest to our guests.

MRS. BENNET. But Lady Lucas herself has often said so, and envied me Jane's beauty.

JANE [*protestingly*]. Mama!

MRS. BENNET. I don't like to boast of my own child, but to be sure, Jane—one doesn't often see anybody better looking. It's what everybody says.

MR. BINGLEY [*with open admiration*]. They are quite right.

[JANE *looks away from him and lowers her eyes.*]

MRS. BENNET. My third daughter will be down presently. Mary is the clever one, always reading and making extracts, as well as constantly practicing on the piano. [NOTE: *If* MARY *is to sing instead of play later, "her singing" may be substituted for "on the piano."*]

ELIZABETH [*trying to change the subject*]. What fine weather we are having, Miss Bingley.

MISS BINGLEY. I find it still a little cool.

ELIZABETH [*glancing at* MR. DARCY, *who stands stiffly by the fireplace*]. Maybe you are right.

MR. BINGLEY [*hastily, sensing the tension*]. Part of my purpose in calling here today was to invite you all to a ball at Netherfield. It is to be a fortnight from now. [*He places his tea cup on the tea table.*]

LYDIA [*delighted*]. Oh, Kitty, did you hear that?

[CATHERINE *giggles happily.*]

LYDIA. I do hope you will invite some of the officers.

MR. BINGLEY [*politely, with a bow to* LYDIA]. If it will please you. [*He turns to* JANE.] Miss Lucas has promised me the first dance. Will you do me the honor of promising me the second? [*He bows.*]

JANE. Thank you, I will. [*She bows her head modestly.*]

MRS. BENNET [*gushingly, to* MR. DARCY, *trying to bring him into the conversation*]. What a charming amusement for young people dancing is, Mr. Darcy!

MR. DARCY [*coldly*]. Yes. And it has the advantage of being in vogue everywhere. Every *savage* can dance. [*He turns to place his cup on the mantel.*]

[MRS. BENNET *is for once taken aback. There is an embarrassed pause. The silence is broken by the entrance of* MARY, U R. *She still has her book.*]

MR. BENNET. May I present our daughter, Miss Mary? Miss Bingley, Mr. Bingley, and Mr. Darcy.

[MARY *comes to* C *and curtsies to* MISS BINGLEY. *The men bow low.*]

MRS. BENNET. Jane, my love, tea for Mary.

[JANE *sees that* MARY *is served with tea.*]

MARY [*on the spoken cue, "—tea for Mary."*]. I am sorry I was not present when you called. I have been reading.

MISS BINGLEY. Indeed!

MARY [*smugly*]. One finds such comfort in a good volume of sensible thoughts. [*She sits on the chair right of the arch* U C.]

MRS. BENNET [*indulgently*]. Mary is the clever one!

[MARY *smirks self-consciously.* MR. BENNET *moves to behind the settee.*]

MISS BINGLEY [*to* MR. DARCY]. What a delightful library *you* have at Pemberley!

MR. DARCY. It has been the work of many generations.

MRS. BENNET. Elizabeth, too, is fond of reading. You should have a great deal in common.

ELIZABETH [*coldly*]. I am sure we never read the same books, nor with the same feeling.

[MR. DARCY *gives* ELIZABETH *a brief nod.* ELIZABETH *turns her head away from him, sharply.*]

MISS BINGLEY [*rising, glancing with distaste at* JANE *and* MR. BINGLEY, *who are engrossed in each other*]. If you will excuse us now. . . . [*She turns to* MR. DARCY.] You spoke of having to write a letter to your sister.

MR. DARCY. Yes.

[*They all rise.*]

MISS BINGLEY. Miss Darcy is such a dear girl! We all think the world of her. [*She turns to* MR. BINGLEY *with assumed archness.*] Do we not, Charles? [*She crosses to* C.]

MR. BINGLEY [*coming to with a start from watching* JANE]. Oh—yes! I'm sure we'll like it here!

MISS BINGLEY [*with emphasis*]. I said you think the world of Miss Darcy, Charles.

MR. BINGLEY. Of course. A nice child.

MRS. BENNET. We shall look forward to seeing you soon again.

LYDIA. At the ball! You won't forget? [*She crosses eagerly to* MR. BINGLEY.]

CATHERINE [*following her*]. Be sure *you* don't forget.

MR. BINGLEY. I'm certain that I shall not.

[LYDIA *and* CATHERINE *giggle happily.*]

MR. BENNET. You have provided them with a topic of conversation for some days to come.

[*The guests have moved toward the door* U R. HILL *comes in* U R.]

HILL [*announcing*]. Mr. Wickham.

LYDIA [*pleased*]. Kitty, Mr. Wickham is calling!

MRS. BENNET [*with an attempt to impress*]. How many callers we have this afternoon! Show him in, Hill.

HILL. Yes, madam.

[HILL *goes out* U R.]

MRS. BENNET. The next time you call, I hope you can take a turn in our garden. It is small, perhaps, but our friends consider it quite delightful.

MR. BINGLEY. I'm sure it is.

[HILL *ushers* MR. WICKHAM *in* U R. *Then she goes out* U R. *He is a handsome young officer, and cuts a dashing figure in his smart uniform. He has undeniable charm of manner, but is untrustworthy and insincere. When he sees the other guests, he pauses* U R C.]

MRS. BENNET [*going toward him*]. Mr. Wickham, have you met our guests? Miss Bingley, Mr. Bingley, Mr. Darcy.

[MR. WICKHAM *bows low.* MISS BINGLEY *drops him a brief curtsey.* MR. BINGLEY *bows. But* MR. DARCY *looks directly at him, and then turns away without acknowledging the introduction.* ELIZABETH *is especially aware of this.*]

MR. DARCY [*to* MRS. BENNET]. We bid you good afternoon.

MRS. BENNET [*upset, realizing something is amiss*]. Oh, I——— Good afternoon!

[MR. BINGLEY *and* MR. DARCY *bow to the ladies, and the ladies curtsey.* MR. WICKHAM *bows to* MISS BINGLEY, *as does* MR. BENNET. *She curtsies to them.* MISS BINGLEY, MR. BINGLEY, *and* MR. DARCY *go out* U R.]

MR. BENNET. Mr. Wickham, I leave you to the tender graces of the ladies while I retire to the library. [*He crosses* U L.]

MR. WICKHAM [*gallantly, with a bow to the ladies*]. I am charmed, I assure you!

[MR. BENNET *goes out* U L.]

MARY. I shall continue with my extracts.

[MARY *goes primly out* D R. MRS. BENNET, MR. WICKHAM, LYDIA, *and* CATHERINE *come to* C *stage.* JANE *sits again at* R C *and takes up her needlework.*]

MR. WICKHAM [*to* MRS. BENNET]. I have called with an invitation from your sister, Mrs. Phillips.

MRS. BENNET. How nice of you!

MR. WICKHAM. She would be pleased to have your daughters at her home for dinner tonight, and perhaps a game of lottery tickets afterward.

LYDIA [*clinging to* MRS. BENNET]. Oh, Mama, say we may go!

CATHERINE [*holding on to her mother's other arm*]. So many of the *officers* will be there in the evening!

MRS. BENNET. But we ourselves have a guest coming for dinner. Your father's cousin, Mr. Collins.

CATHERINE. He won't care to see *us*.

ELIZABETH [*who has remained by the fireplace*]. We should be here to greet him.

MR. WICKHAM. But, Miss Elizabeth, I wish especially that you should attend.

ELIZABETH. Thank you, but I think not. [*She sits on the bench* D L.]

LYDIA [*going to* MR. WICKHAM *and taking his arm*]. *I* shall go. You may escort me there yourself!

CATHERINE [*taking his other arm*]. I'll go, too. Do say yes, Mama.

MRS. BENNET [*yielding*]. Very well. [*She shakes her finger at them coyly.*] Mind—you behave yourselves, and don't flirt with the officers!

LYDIA. You *know* we don't flirt!

MRS. BENNET [*starting for the door* D R]. Then get your wraps. I must see about dinner.

[MRS. BENNET *goes out* D R. LYDIA *and* CATHERINE *follow her to the door.*]

LYDIA. We won't be a minute, Mr. Wickham.

CATHERINE. I wish *I* had a new bonnet to wear!

[LYDIA *and* CATHERINE *go out* D R, *chatting excitedly.* MR. WICKHAM *crosses toward the settee.*]

ELIZABETH. Mr. Wickham, don't answer if you find the question objectionable, but did Mr. Darcy acknowledge your greeting just now?

MR. WICKHAM. He did not.

ELIZABETH. I thought him very rude.

JANE [*to* ELIZABETH]. Perhaps we are mistaken. He seemed a polite gentleman, though rather silent.

ELIZABETH. Oh, Jane, you're too sweet—you never see a fault in anybody! *I* thought him very disagreeable—as if it would hurt him to open his lips.

MR. WICKHAM [*to* ELIZABETH]. Are you much acquainted with Mr. Darcy?

ELIZABETH. As much as I ever wish to be!

MR. WICKHAM. I have no right to give *my* opinion. I've known him too long and too well to be a fair judge.

ELIZABETH [*surprised, rising, moving to the armchair right of the fireplace*]. You have!

MR. WICKHAM. My father was steward of Pemberley, the Darcy estate, and the present Mr. Darcy's father had a deep attachment for me.

ELIZABETH. Then why does he ignore you? [*She sits in the armchair.*]

MR. WICKHAM. The late Mr. Darcy was one of the best men that have ever breathed. But his son is a very different sort of man.

ELIZABETH. His abominable pride is quite disgusting.

MR. WICKHAM [*continuing*]. A military life is not what I was intended for. In fact, I was brought up for the church.

ELIZABETH. Indeed!

MR. WICKHAM. I should at this time have been in the possession of a most valuable clerical living, had it pleased the gentlemen we were speaking of just now. [*He speaks agitatedly, and walks* U R C *and back to* D L C.]

ELIZABETH. You mean, Mr. Darcy interfered?

MR. WICKHAM. The living was bequeathed to me by his father, but it was given elsewhere.

ELIZABETH. Good heavens!

JANE. How could his will be disregarded?

MR. WICKHAM. Mr. Darcy *chose* to doubt his father's intentions.

ELIZABETH. This is quite shocking! He deserves to be publicly disgraced!

MR. WICKHAM. Some time or other he *will* be, but it shall not be by *me*. Till I can forget his good father, I can never defy or expose *him*.

ELIZABETH. What can have induced him to behave so cruelly?

MR. WICKHAM. A thorough, determined dislike of me—a dislike which I can only attribute to jealousy.

ELIZABETH. I hadn't thought Mr. Darcy as bad as this.

JANE. How can Mr. Bingley be friendly with such a man? Surely, there must be some mistake.

MR. WICKHAM [*crossing to* ELIZABETH]. Mr. Darcy can please when he chooses. [*He takes* ELIZABETH'S *hand.*] Your sympathy is very comforting to me.

ELIZABETH [*rising, and withdrawing her hand quickly*]. What could I do but sympathize!

[LYDIA *and* CATHERINE *come in* D R, *wearing their wraps and bonnets. They cross excitedly to* C *stage.*]

LYDIA. Do you notice my new bonnet?

MR. WICKHAM [*politely, moving to* C *stage*]. Most becoming, Miss Lydia.

CATHERINE [*taking his arm*]. Come, let us be off.

MR. WICKHAM [*turning again to* ELIZABETH]. I hope I shall see you soon, Miss Elizabeth. [*He turns to* JANE.] And you, too, Miss Jane.

JANE [*rising*]. Thank you.

[LYDIA *takes his other arm.* MR. WICKHAM *bows.* JANE *and* ELIZABETH *curtsey. Calling "good-byes,"* LYDIA *and* CATHERINE *go out* U R *with* MR. WICKHAM. *As soon as they have gone,* JANE *hurries excitedly to* ELIZABETH *and they sit near the fireplace for a confidential chat.* ELIZABETH *sits on the bench, while* JANE *sits in the armchair.*]

JANE [*eagerly*]. What did you think of him?

ELIZABETH. Mr. Wickham?

JANE [*eagerly*]. No. Mr—Bingley.

ELIZABETH. What do *you* think of him? He never took his eyes from you.

JANE [*softly*]. I think he is just what a young man ought to be. Sensible, good-humored, lively. And I never saw such a happy manner!

ELIZABETH. He is also handsome, which a young man ought to be if he possibly can.

JANE. I'm very much flattered by his asking me for a dance. I didn't expect such a compliment.

ELIZABETH. And why not?

JANE [*modestly*]. Oh, Elizabeth!

ELIZABETH. What could be more natural than his asking you? He couldn't help seeing how pretty you are.

JANE. Dear Lizzy! Do you really think so?

ELIZABETH. You have my word for it, and I give you leave to like him.

JANE [*worried, rising, moving toward* C *stage*]. If only Mama——

ELIZABETH. I know, dear—but we can't change Mama. She will always be the same.

[MRS. BENNET *comes in* D R.]

MRS. BENNET [*coming to* C]. The girls have gone?

JANE. Yes, Mama. [*She sits on the settee.*]

MRS. BENNET. What a charming man Mr. Bingley is! And did you notice, Lizzy, how taken he was with Jane? [*She beams on* JANE.]

ELIZABETH [*dryly*]. I noticed.

MRS. BENNET. That proud Mr. Darcy paid little attention to *you*, Lizzy. But no matter how large his fortune, it is no ill-luck to be disliked by *him*.

ELIZABETH. I agree.

MRS. BENNET. He is a disagreeable, horrid man. I quite detest him.

[HILL *comes in* U R.]

HILL. Mr. William Collins, madam.

MRS. BENNET. So soon! Lizzy, go fetch your father.

[ELIZABETH *hurries out* U L.]

MRS. BENNET [*to* HILL]. Show him in.

HILL. Yes, madam.

[HILL *goes out* U R.]

MRS. BENNET [*moving* U C]. I hope my nerves will survive his visit.

[HILL *ushers* MR. COLLINS *in* U R. *He is a tall, heavy-set young clergyman, pompous and pedantic, with absurdly formal manners. He is continually bowing. Yet, he is extremely serv-ile whenever to be so is to his advantage.*]

HILL. Mr. Collins, madam.

[MR. COLLINS *comes to* U R C *and bows profusely to* MRS. BEN-NET, *and then to* JANE, *who rises.*]

MR. COLLINS. Ladies.

[MR. BENNET *enters* U L *and moves to* U C *stage.*]

MR. BENNET. Good afternoon, Cousin. [*He bows to* MR. COL-LINS.]

MR. COLLINS [*pompously, bowing*]. Your servant, sir. I trust I do not intrude upon your good lady by my visit.

MR. BENNET. Allow me to present my good lady, and my daughter, Miss Jane.

[MR. BENNET *and* JANE *curtsey, and* MR. COLLINS *bows very low to each.*]

MR. COLLINS. I am honored. [*He bows again to each lady.*]

MRS. BENNET [*coolly*]. Won't you be seated, Mr. Collins? [*She moves to the settee.*]

MR. COLLINS. Thank you.

[MR. COLLINS *sits stiffly in the armchair* R C. MRS. BENNET *sits on the settee.* JANE *sits next to* MRS. BENNET, *with her embroidery.* MR. BENNET *stands right of the settee.*]

MR. BENNET. I trust you had a pleasant journey?

MR. COLLINS. Very pleasant, thank you. I am looking forward to the pleasure of meeting your other daughters, for I have heard much of their beauty.

MRS. BENNET [*warming toward him*]. How nice of you to say so!

MR. COLLINS [*ogling* JANE]. In the case of Miss Jane, fame has fallen short of the truth.

[JANE *lowers her head modestly.*]

MRS. BENNET [*beaming*]. Indeed, that is what everybody says.

MR. COLLINS. I do not doubt that in due time you will see them all well disposed in—marriage. [*He simpers at* JANE.]

MRS. BENNET. You are very kind, I am sure, and I wish with all my heart it may be so, for else they will be destitute enough. Things are settled so oddly. [*She manages a tear in her voice, and looks at* MR. COLLINS *reproachfully.*]

MR. BENNET [*warningly*]. My dear, let us not go into that. [*He moves above the settee and over to the fireplace.*]

MR. COLLINS. You allude, perhaps, to the entail of this estate?

MRS. BENNET. I do, indeed! It is a grievous affair to my poor girls, you must confess.

MR. COLLINS. Quite right—and I was thinking——[*He glances coyly at* JANE, *who lowers her head.*]

MRS. BENNET [*quickly*]. Not that I mean to find fault with *you.*

MR. COLLINS. I am very sensible, madam, of the hardship to my fair cousins. But I can assure you that I come prepared to admire them. Ah—yes—and even more.

[MR. COLLINS *smiles fatuously at* JANE *again, and she lowers her eyes.*]

MRS. BENNET. You are most kind.

[ELIZABETH *comes in* U L *and crosses to* C *stage.* MR. COLLINS *rises and eyes her appreciatively.*]

MR. BENNET [*making the introduction, standing by the fireplace*]. Our cousin, Mr. Collins. My second daughter, Miss Elizabeth.

[ELIZABETH *curtsies.* MR. COLLINS *bows deeply.*]

MR. COLLINS [*ogling her*]. I am delighted to make your acquaintance. [*He bows again.*]

ELIZABETH [*staring straight back at him*]. Thank you. Mama, shall Jane and I oblige you by making sure that Mr. Collins' room is in readiness?

MRS. BENNET. I wish you would, my dear.

[ELIZABETH *goes* U R. MR. COLLINS *follows her with his eyes.* JANE *rises and joins* ELIZABETH U R. *They go out* U R.]

MR. COLLINS [*confidentially, moving to* C *stage*]. As I said, I came prepared to admire your daughters. [*He glances* U R, *where the girls have gone out.*] My patroness, Lady Catherine de Bourgh, has condescended to advise me that a young clergyman like myself needs a wife.

MRS. BENNET [*becoming enthusiastic about him*]. Oh, Mr. Collins!

[MR. BENNET *clears his throat noisily.*]

MR. COLLINS. And it is my hope that a mistress for my home may be found here at Longbourn.

MR. BENNET [*dryly*]. So that is what you meant by making amends!

MR. COLLINS. It is, my dear sir. [*He bows to* MR. BENNET.]

MRS. BENNET. What a compliment to our girls, Mr. Bennet!
[*She speaks to* MR. COLLINS.] As to my *younger* daughters,
I can't take it upon me to say—but I don't *know* of any pre-
possession.

MR. COLLINS. And as for Miss Jane?

MRS. BENNET. I feel it encumbent on me to hint that Jane is
likely to be soon engaged.

MR. COLLINS. I see. In point of seniority, Miss Elizabeth is next.

MRS. BENNET [*eagerly*]. She is quite unattached.

MR. COLLINS [*thoughtfully*]. A very charming young lady. [*He
turns upstage a few steps, turns, and comes back.*] I am cautious of appearing forward and precipitate. At present, I will
say no more, but perhaps when we are better acquainted——

MRS. BENNET [*rising, moving to him*]. My *dear* Mr. Collins!

MR. COLLINS. Since I am assured that my welcome is cordial, I
shall instruct your man to bring in my bags.

[MR. COLLINS *bows and goes out* U R.]

MRS. BENNET [*happily, crossing toward the door* U R *and then
turning back to* C *stage*]. Did you hear what he said, Mr.
Bennet? He wants to marry one of our girls!

MR. BENNET [*dryly*]. I still have my hearing.

MRS. BENNET [*figuring it all out*]. Since Mr. Bingley is so
taken with Jane, Elizabeth will be the *perfect* choice for Mr.
Collins!

MR. BENNET. Madam, you are as silly as your daughters. [*He
starts* U L, *toward the library.*]

MRS. BENNET [*offended*]. I'm astonished that you can think
your own children silly. They are all of them very clever.

MR. BENNET [*pausing* U L]. You must excuse me if I differ
about the three youngest.

MRS. BENNET. You mustn't expect them to have the sense of their mother.

MR. BENNET. Heaven forbid!

[MR. BENNET *throws up his hands with mock horror and goes out* U L.]

MRS. BENNET. I can't believe it! Two of my daughters practically married!

[MRS. BENNET *stands at* C *stage with her hands clasped ecstatically.*]

CURTAIN

Act Two—Scene One

AT RISE OF CURTAIN: *The scene is the same. It is morning, two weeks later, a few days after the ball at Netherfield. A small table has been placed between the armchair and the bench near the fireplace, and* MR. BENNET *and* MR. COLLINS *are playing checkers.*]

MR. BENNET [*who is seated on the bench*]. Your move, Mr. Collins.

MR. COLLINS [*starting out of a reverie*]. Oh, yes! [*He moves a checker.*] I was lost in thought.

MR. BENNET [*dryly*]. "Lost"—an excellent choice of words. [*He moves a checker and waits awhile.*] Your move, Mr. Collins.

MR. COLLINS. Eh? [*He moves a checker.*]

[MR. BENNET *moves as* MRS. BENNET *comes in* D R *with a vase of spring flowers.*]

MRS. BENNET [*brightly, moving to* C *and holding up the vase*]. Aren't these flowers beautiful, Mr. Collins?

MR. COLLINS [*condescendingly*]. Quite passable—for a small garden. My own humble abode is separated only by a lane from Lady Catherine's beautiful estate, where there is a veritable profusion of bloom.

MRS. BENNET [*crossing* U C *and placing the vase on the table*]. I dare say Lady Catherine is a very agreeable woman.

MR. COLLINS. She is thought to be proud by many, but I have never seen anything but affability in her.

MR. BENNET [*with strained patience*]. Your move, Mr. Collins.

[MR. COLLINS *moves, as if annoyed by the interruption.*]

MRS. BENNET [*crossing* R, *picking up a piece of embroidery work from the desk, and sitting in the armchair* R C]. I think you said she is a widow? Has she any family?

MR. COLLINS. One daughter.

MRS. BENNET. What sort of young lady is she? Is she handsome?

MR. BENNET [*his patience wearing thin*]. Your move.

MR. COLLINS [*moving a checker*]. A most charming young lady, indeed, but unfortunately of a sickly constitution.

MRS. BENNET. Has she been presented at court?

MR. COLLINS. Her indifferent state of health unhappily prevents that. As I told Lady Catherine, the British court is deprived of its brightest ornament. [*He smirks.*]

MR. BENNET [*smartly jumping several of* MR. COLLINS' *checkers*]. Your move.

MR. COLLINS [*hastily trying to make the proper move and speak at the same time*]. Her ladyship seemed pleased with the idea.

MR. BENNET [*amused*]. You will observe, Mr. Collins, that I have your last king in a corner. [*He rises.*]

MR. COLLINS [*dismissing it with a wave of his hand*]. Ah, yes! A trivial game. [*He takes up a book from the checker table as he rises and moves back of the settee to* C *stage.*]

MR. BENNET. If you'll excuse me, I shall spend a little time in my library.

[MR. BENNET *bows to* MR. COLLINS *and goes out* U L, *carrying the checker table with him.*]

MR. COLLINS. I thought perhaps your daughters would gather in here this morning while I read aloud from this elevating volume—[*He eyes it fondly.*]—"Fordyce's Sermons."

MRS. BENNET. How interesting! The girls would have loved it —but they are out. Jane, as you know, is still visiting at Netherfield.

MR. COLLINS [*with a smirk*]. Mr. Bingley has taken quite an interest.

MRS. BENNET. How happy I will be, Mr. Collins, when my daughters are well settled.

MR. COLLINS. May I hope, madam, to have a word with Miss Elizabeth this morning?

MRS. BENNET [*fluttering her embroidery*]. Oh, dear, yes, certainly! I'm sure Lizzy will be very happy!

MR. COLLINS. In that case, would you let me know when Miss Elizabeth returns?

MRS. BENNET. I shall speak to her as soon as she comes in.

[MR. COLLINS *bows and goes out* U C. MRS. BENNET, *very much elated, hurries to the library door* U L.]

MRS. BENNET [*calling*]. My dear! [*When there is no answer, she knocks loudly.*]

MR. BENNET [*off* U L]. Go away!

MRS. BENNET [*turning away*]. How can you understand my feelings, Mr. Bennet? *You* are not a *mother*.

[ELIZABETH *and* CHARLOTTE *come in* U R *and move to* C.]

CHARLOTTE [*with a curtsey*]. Good morning, Mrs. Bennet.

MRS. BENNET [*moving to the settee*]. How nice to see you, my dear Charlotte!

CHARLOTTE. I promised Papa I'd bake some mince pies, and nothing would do but that I try the recipe *your* cook uses.

MRS. BENNET. Cook will be flattered. [*She crosses close to* ELIZABETH *and speaks urgently to her.*] Lizzy, Mr. Collins wishes to speak to you at once. [*She nods* U C.] He is in the garden.

ELIZABETH. A little fresh air will do him good.

MRS. BENNET. I insist that you see him immediately.

ELIZABETH [*politely*]. Yes, Mama.

MRS. BENNET [*going* D R]. I shall ask Cook to have the recipe ready for you, Charlotte.

[MRS. BENNET *goes out* D R. CHARLOTTE *starts to follow.*]

ELIZABETH. Don't hurry away, Charlotte. [*She pulls* CHARLOTTE *over to the settee and sits with her.*] I want to talk to you about the ball at Netherfield.

CHARLOTTE. Everyone is saying how much attention Mr. Bingley paid to Jane.

ELIZABETH. It *did* seem as if he admired her.

CHARLOTTE. Is Jane happy?

ELIZABETH. Very happy. But you know how she is, so composed that a man could never guess her real feelings.

CHARLOTTE. It's a mistake for a woman to conceal her affection with too much skill. Mr. Bingley likes your sister, undoubtedly, but he may never do more than like her if she doesn't encourage him.

ELIZABETH. But she does encourage him, as much as her nature will allow. If a woman is partial to a man, he must find it out.

CHARLOTTE. In nine cases out of ten, a woman had better show more affection than she feels. The time to fall in love is after she is sure of him.

ELIZABETH. Not Jane. Her love knows no design.

CHARLOTTE. *You* didn't fare so well at the ball, Lizzy.

[ELIZABETH *gets up and walks toward the fireplace.*]

ELIZABETH. That hateful Mr. Darcy! I overheard him talking about me.

CHARLOTTE. You *did?* Oh, Lizzy!

ELIZABETH. Mr. Bingley suggested that he ask me to dance. Our fine Mr. Darcy said, "She is tolerable, but not handsome enough to *tempt* me."

CHARLOTTE. Poor Eliza, to be only just tolerable!

ELIZABETH. Indeed, if he were to *like* me, I should be quite put out.

[MARY *comes in* D R *with a book, as usual.*]

CHARLOTTE. Hello, Mary—reading again?

MARY [*kissing* CHARLOTTE *briefly on the cheek*]. Hello, Charlotte. [*She sits in the armchair at* R C.]

CHARLOTTE [*turning to* ELIZABETH]. In a way, Mr. Darcy's pride is understandable. A fine young man with family, fortune, and everything in his favor has a *right* to be proud.

ELIZABETH. I could forgive *his* pride, if he had not mortified *mine.*

MARY [*looking up from her book*]. Pride is a very common failing, I believe. By all that I have ever read, I am convinced that human nature is particularly prone to it. Indeed, there are few of us who do not cherish a feeling of self-complacency on the score of some quality or other, real or imaginary. [*This lecture is delivered in a prim, superior tone.*]

CHARLOTTE [*politely*]. Oh, yes, indeed! [*She rises.*] I must get the recipe before I leave. [*She seems eager to escape* MARY'S *lecture.*]

MARY [*continuing*]. Vanity and pride are different things, though the words are often used synonymously. A person may be proud without being vain.

CHARLOTTE [*as she goes* D R]. I'll see you again before I go.

ELIZABETH. Please do.

[CHARLOTTE *hurries out* D R.]

MARY [*continuing*]. Pride relates more to our opinion of ourselves—vanity to what we would have others think of us.

ELIZABETH [*impatiently, crossing to the settee*]. *I* know you are clever, Mary.

[LYDIA *and* CATHERINE *are heard giggling off* U R. MARY *rises and closes her book.*]

MARY. The idle chatter of my younger sisters has no appeal for me.

[MARY *goes out* D R. LYDIA *and* CATHERINE *come in* U R *with* MR. WICKHAM, *each clinging to one of his arms. They each have a book.* LYDIA *carries a parasol. It is closed, but in* LYDIA'S *flighty hands it is a dangerous weapon.*]

LYDIA [*gayly, as they come to* C]. We met Mr. Wickham in front of the library, and he offered to escort us home.

[LYDIA *waves her parasol.* MR. WICKHAM *sidesteps it and bows to* ELIZABETH, *who curtsies back.*]

CATHERINE [*giggling*]. You can imagine how all the other girls envied us.

LYDIA. La! What fun, to have everybody looking at us!

[*Again* LYDIA *gestures with the parasol, and again* MR. WICKHAM *sidesteps.*]

MR. WICKHAM. I fear Miss Elizabeth does not envy you overmuch. In vain have I entreated *her* to take a walk with me.

ELIZABETH. Indeed, sir, I have not refused you from intent, but only because I was occupied at the time.

LYDIA [*moving toward* ELIZABETH]. *I* am never too busy to go walking with a handsome man in a red coat!

[LYDIA *smiles up at* MR. WICKHAM, *waving her parasol flirtatiously. This time it is* ELIZABETH *who has to sidestep it.*]

CATHERINE [*moving* D R]. We must tell Mama all the news from Meryton.

LYDIA [*joining* CATHERINE D R]. Mama loves a bit of gossip.

[LYDIA *swings her parasol, nearly hitting* CATHERINE. *They go out* D R, LYDIA *giving* MR. WICKHAM *a flirtatious nod as she leaves.*]

ELIZABETH [*crossing to him*]. Won't you sit down, Mr. Wickham?

MR. WICKHAM. Thank you, no. I must be on my way.

ELIZABETH. We missed you at the Netherfield ball.

MR. WICKHAM. Unfortunately, business in the city took me away at just that time.

ELIZABETH. I understand. [*She moves back to the fireplace and sits on the bench.*]

MR. WICKHAM [*quickly, moving toward her*]. Not that I have any wish to avoid Mr. Darcy. It is the other way around.

ELIZABETH. Of course. I have a mind to walk with you a little way, since you teased me about refusing your invitations.

MR. WICKHAM [*with a deep bow*]. I shall be honored.

ELIZABETH [*hesitantly*]. We expect Jane back from Netherfield this morning. And I promised Mama I would speak with my cousin, Mr. Collins.

MR. WICKHAM. You can do that later.

ELIZABETH [*with a laugh*]. Very much later. He has recently been given a parish by Lady Catherine de Bourgh, and he can talk of little else. [*She rises and moves to* C.]

MR. WICKHAM. Her daughter, Miss de Bourgh, will have a very large fortune. It is believed that she and Mr. Darcy will marry some day.

ELIZABETH. I am pleased to hear it. From what I have heard of Lady Catherine, a daughter of hers is not likely to make *any* man happy!

MR. WICKHAM [*laughing*]. Not likely!

[*From off* D R *comes the sound of* MARY'S *music. If there is a piano in a place where it is not visible to the audience,* MARY *may practice on it in a laborious, stilted way, pausing very often, and starting again. If preferred, she may sing instead. This may be scales, or some Scotch or Irish air. Whatever it is,* MARY'S *rendering is both comic and annoying.*]

ELIZABETH. Mary is practicing again! [*She starts toward* U C.] Let's take a short cut through the garden.

[ELIZABETH *and* MR. WICKHAM *start out* U C *as* HILL *comes in* U R.]

HILL. Miss Jane is back—with Mr. Bingley, his sister, and Mr. Darcy.
ELIZABETH [*to* HILL]. I'll see her after the guests are gone.

[ELIZABETH *and* MR. WICKHAM *go out* U C. HILL *shrugs and starts out* U R *as* JANE, MISS BINGLEY, MR. BINGLEY, *and* MR. DARCY *come in* U R. *For the moment,* MARY'S *music has stopped.* HILL *continues out* U R.]

JANE [*coming to* C *with her guests*]. Sit down, my dear Caroline. And you, too. [*She nods toward* MR. BINGLEY *and* MR. DARCY.] I shall let Mama know you have been kind enough to drive me home.
MISS BINGLEY. Don't disturb her if she is occupied. We can't stay long. [*She sits on the settee.*]
JANE. Mama will want to thank you for your kindness to me.

[JANE *goes out* D R. MR. DARCY *walks* D L *and remains standing.* MR. BINGLEY *sits in the armchair* R C.]

MISS BINGLEY. Jane Bennet is really a very sweet girl.
MR. BINGLEY [*glancing* D R]. She is all of that.

MISS BINGLEY. I wish with all my heart that she were well settled. But with such a mother, and such low connections, I'm afraid there is no chance of it.

[MARY'S *music starts again.* MISS BINGLEY *puts her hands over her ears and shudders.*]

MR. BINGLEY [*staunchly*]. If she had no connections, I would not think one jot less of her.

MR. DARCY. Nevertheless, how can she expect to marry a man of any consideration in the world?

MISS BINGLEY. You are right, Mr. Darcy. Jane was quite a success at our ball, but—[*She pauses and looks sharply at* MR. DARCY.]—I observed that Elizabeth Bennet was not very much of an attraction to you.

MR. DARCY. Why do you say that?

MISS BINGLEY. You made no effort to dance with her.

MR. DARCY [*stiffly*]. I detest dancing.

[*There is a pause.* MR. DARCY *turns away and stares out front.*]

MISS BINGLEY. Why so thoughtful, Mr. Darcy?

MR. DARCY. No reason at all.

MISS BINGLEY. This must be serious!

MR. DARCY. I was thinking of the very great pleasure which a pair of fine eyes in the face of a pretty woman can bestow.

MISS BINGLEY [*flirtatiously*]. Oh, Mr. Darcy! What lady has the credit of inspiring such reflections?

MR. DARCY [*as if hating to admit it*]. Miss Elizabeth Bennet.

MISS BINGLEY. I am astonished! When am I to wish you joy?

MR. DARCY. A lady's imagination is very wondrous; it jumps from admiration to love and from love to matrimony in a moment.

MISS BINGLEY [*with a laugh*]. You will have a charming mother-in-law!

MR. DARCY. You *know* I'm not serious.

MISS BINGLEY [*teasingly*]. I hope you give your mother-in-law a few hints as to the advantage of holding her tongue; and if you can, do cure the younger girls of running after the officers.

[MARY'S *music starts again.*]

MISS BINGLEY. Oh! *Which* one is responsible for that?

MR. DARCY. I couldn't say.

[JANE *comes in* D R *with* MRS. BENNET. MR. BINGLEY *rises, and he and* MR. DARCY *bow.*]

MRS. BENNET [*gushing, as she moves to* C *with* JANE]. My dear Miss Bingley! My dear sirs! How extremely kind you've been to Jane!

MR. BINGLEY. The kindness was on Miss Jane's side.

MISS BINGLEY [*politely*]. We have found her very pleasant company.

JANE [*with a curtsey*]. Thank you.

MISS BINGLEY [*rising*]. Are you ready to return now, Charles?

MR. BINGLEY [*reluctantly, his eyes on* JANE]. So soon?

MRS. BENNET [*quickly*]. Jane, my love, didn't Mr. Bingley once express a wish to see our garden?

JANE. But, Mama——

MR. BINGLEY [*eagerly, crossing close to* JANE]. I did, madam. Will you show it to me, Miss Jane?

MRS. BENNET [*quickly, before* JANE *can reply*]. Of course she will.

[MR. BINGLEY *and* JANE *start* U C.]

MRS. BENNET [*moving toward* MISS BINGLEY]. Miss Bingley, Mr. Darcy, and I will have a nice little chat.

[MARY'S *music takes on renewed force.*]

MISS BINGLEY [*hastily*]. Do you mind if I see the garden, too?
[*She joins* JANE *and* MR. BINGLEY.]

MRS. BENNET. Oh . . . Er—by all means. And you, Mr.
Darcy?

MR. DARCY. Thank you. I shall remain here.

[MR. DARCY *turns, picks up a book from the bench* D L, *and
stands stiffly.* JANE *and* MR. BINGLEY *go out* U C. MISS BING-
LEY *hurries out after them.*]

MISS BINGLEY [*as she goes out*]. Wait for me, Charles!

MRS. BENNET [*at a loss for conversation*]. You are a great
reader, Mr. Darcy?

MR. DARCY [*not turning, his back to* MRS. BENNET]. Yes,
madam.

[*There is a pause.*]

MRS. BENNET. Quite a pleasant day, isn't it?

MR. DARCY. It *was.*

[*There is another pause.*]

MRS. BENNET. Are you remaining long at Netherfield?

MR. DARCY. I cannot say.

MRS. BENNET. Oh! . . . [*There is another pause. Then she
continues in an acid tone.*] If you will excuse me, I shall
leave you to your reading.

MR. DARCY. Certainly, madam.

[MRS. BENNET *looks at his back a moment, makes a face, and
goes out* D R. MR. DARCY *turns the pages idly, paying little
attention to them. After a moment,* ELIZABETH *comes in* U C.
She stops short upon seeing MR. DARCY.]

ELIZABETH [*coolly*]. Good morning, Mr. Darcy.

MR. DARCY [*turning, bowing*]. Good morning, Miss Elizabeth. We have brought Miss Jane home.

ELIZABETH [*coming down to the armchair* R C]. I've just seen her. I'm sure Jane had a most delightful time.

MR. DARCY. Quite. [*He puts the book on the mantel.*]

[*There is a long pause. Both are uncomfortable, and do not know what to say.*]

ELIZABETH. It is *your* turn to say something now, Mr. Darcy. You might make some remark about the weather. [*She sits in the armchair at* R C.]

MR. DARCY. Consider it made. [*He sits in the armchair at* L *stage.*]

ELIZABETH. One must speak a *little,* you know.

MR. DARCY. And in some cases, the less said the better.

[*There is another pause.*]

ELIZABETH [*with determination*]. Nevertheless, I shall introduce the next topic. I've just had a short walk with a mutual friend of ours—Mr. Wickham.

MR. DARCY [*in a constrained tone*]. Mr. Wickham has a way of *making* friends—whether he may be equally capable of *retaining* them is less certain.

ELIZABETH [*with emphasis*]. He has been so unlucky as to lose *your* friendship, Mr. Darcy, and through no fault of his own.

MR. DARCY [*rising, moving toward the settee*]. Miss Bennet, do not judge my character when you know so little about me.

ELIZABETH. I have seen—and heard—enough.

MR. DARCY [*earnestly*]. All my life I have tried to avoid weakness of any kind.

ELIZABETH. Such as vanity and pride?

MR. DARCY. Vanity is a weakness, indeed. But pride—that is a different matter.

ELIZABETH. I suppose you never allow yourself to be blinded by prejudice?

MR. DARCY. I hope not. [*He crosses to left of her chair.*] Do *you*, Miss Elizabeth?

ELIZABETH [*rising, slightly indignant*]. I? Certainly not.

MR. DARCY [*abruptly*]. Then let us drop the subject for the moment. [*He moves to the settee.*]

[MRS. BENNET *and* CHARLOTTE *come in* D R.]

CHARLOTTE [*as she comes in*]. If I'm ever to get the mince pies baked, I really must be on my way.

[CHARLOTTE *stops short when she sees* MR. DARCY. *He turns and bows.*]

MR. DARCY. Miss Lucas.

CHARLOTTE [*with a curtsey*]. How—nice—to see you again, Mr. Darcy.

[CHARLOTTE *glances over at* ELIZABETH, *who wrinkles up her nose with distaste.*]

MRS. BENNET. Charlotte is going home to do some baking. *My* girls are never allowed in the kitchen—but I'm sure your dear mother knows what is best for you, Charlotte. [*She pats* CHARLOTTE'S *arm in sympathy.*]

ELIZABETH [*staunchly, moving to her*]. Charlotte is very clever —and I envy her.

[MR. DARCY *moves back of the settee to left of it on* ELIZABETH'S *cross.*]

CHARLOTTE [*kissing her*]. Thank you, dear Lizzy. Good-bye, Mrs. Bennet. [*She curtsies to* MRS. BENNET.] And you, Mr. Darcy. [*She curtsies to* MR. DARCY.]

[MR. DARCY *bows to her.* CHARLOTTE *crosses* U R *with* ELIZA-BETH, *who sees her out.* MRS. BENNET *is at* R C *as* MISS BING-LEY, JANE, *and* MR. BINGLEY *enter* U C. *They move to* C *stage.*]

MRS. BENNET [*to* MR. DARCY, *as* ELIZABETH *goes out with* CHARLOTTE]. Elizabeth has such a sympathetic nature.

MISS BINGLEY [*politely, as she enters*]. A delightful garden.

JANE. It's small, but we enjoy it.

MR. BINGLEY. I'm sorry we must leave so soon.

JANE. We hope you will come again.

MISS BINGLEY. Thank you.

MR. BINGLEY [*his eyes on* JANE]. You may depend on it.

MRS. BENNET. Dear Jane has so enjoyed her visit.

MISS BINGLEY. We enjoyed having her.

[*The ladies curtsey, the men bow, and* MISS BINGLEY, MR. BING-LEY, *and* MR. DARCY *go out* U R, *amid an ad lib chatter of* "*good-byes.*"]

MRS. BENNET [*happily, to* JANE]. My dear, the way he smiled at you!

JANE [*protestingly*]. Mama!

MRS. BENNET [*coyly*]. You may tell Mama all about it.

[MRS. BENNET *leads* JANE *to the door* D R, *and then turns to* ELIZABETH, *who re-enters* U R *and moves to right of the arm-chair* R C.]

MRS. BENNET. Lizzy, have you spoken with Mr. Collins yet?

ELIZABETH. Not yet.

MRS. BENNET. Then do it at once.

[MR. COLLINS *comes in* U C.]

MR. COLLINS [*a little stiffly, as he moves to* C *stage*]. I have been waiting, but I fear, Mrs. Bennet, that you forgot my request.

MRS. BENNET. Indeed not! I was but this minute reminding Lizzy that you wished to speak to her. Come, Jane. [*She is about to go out.*]

ELIZABETH [*going* D R]. Dear Mama, don't go. I beg of you to stay. Mr. Collins must excuse me. He can have nothing to say to me that anybody need not hear. [*She is a little panicky.*]

MRS. BENNET. Nonsense, Lizzy! Stay where you are.

ELIZABETH [*pleadingly*]. Please, Mama——

MR. COLLINS [*smirking*]. Such modesty!

MRS. BENNET. Lizzy, I *insist* upon your staying and hearing Mr. Collins.

[MRS. BENNET *hurries* JANE *out* D R. ELIZABETH *looks about frantically.*]

MR. COLLINS [*moving slowly toward her, with a silly smirk on his face*]. Believe me, my dear Miss Elizabeth, your modesty adds to your other perfections. You would have been less amiable in my eyes had there *not* been this little—unwillingness.

ELIZABETH [*eyeing him warily as he advances toward her*]. Oh! [*She deftly sweeps past him and over to the settee.*]

MR. COLLINS [*following her*]. Allow me to assure you that I have your respected mother's permission for this address.

ELIZABETH [*faintly*]. You have? [*She sees nothing else to do but sit, so she does, resignedly, on the far left end of the settee.*]

MR. COLLINS [*sliding on to the right end of the settee*]. Almost as soon as I entered this house, I singled you out as the companion of my future life. But before I let my feelings run away with me, I will state my reasons for coming here expressly to select a wife.

[ELIZABETH *looks up at him, rather startled, as he moves a little closer to her.*]

MR. COLLINS. First, I think it is the right thing for a clergyman to set the example of matrimony in his parish. [*He moves a little closer, much to* ELIZABETH'S *consternation.*] Secondly, that it will add greatly to my happiness. [*He moves closer.*] And thirdly, that it is the particular advice and recommendation of my patroness, Lady Catherine de Bourgh, who twice has condescended to give me her opinion—*unasked.* She believes that the wife I choose should be a gentlewoman —an active, useful sort of person, not brought up high, but able to make a small income go a long ways. I am well aware that one thousand pounds with four per cent is all that will be yours when your mother dies. But I assure you that I will never reproach you on that score. And now, nothing remains for me but to prove to you the violence of my affection.

[ELIZABETH *has listened to his recital, first with alarm, and then with amusement.* MR. COLLINS, *on the last line, slips from the settee to one knee in front of her, and awkwardly tries to take* ELIZABETH'S *hand.*]

ELIZABETH [*rising, and drawing away, toward* D L]. You are too hasty. I thank you for your generous offer—but I must decline it.

MR. COLLINS [*with a touch of coyness, rising from his kneeling position*]. Come, come—I know—it is usual for a young lady to act embarrassed and unwilling, when all the time her heart is fluttering with wild panic. [*He starts toward her.*]

ELIZABETH [*backing around the left end of the settee and behind it, to* C *stage*]. Upon my word, sir, you are a hard man to discourage.

MR. COLLINS [*following her*]. I shall lead you to the altar ere long.

ELIZABETH [*backing toward* R C *as* MR. COLLINS *still follows her*]. But I am perfectly serious in my refusal. *You* could not make me happy—and *I* am the last woman in the world who would make you so.

MR. COLLINS [*trying to take her in his arms*]. My dear Elizabeth!

ELIZABETH [*eluding him again and moving over in front of the settee*]. Were your friend, Lady Catherine, to know me, I am sure she would find me in every respect unqualified for the situation.

MR. COLLINS [*following her*]. Ah, Miss Elizabeth—it is your wish to increase my love by suspense, such as most elegant females do. I beg of you, hold me off no longer. Confess your love for me.

ELIZABETH [*tired of being pursued, standing her ground, just back of the left end of the settee, and speaking angrily*]. Really, Mr. Collins! Can I speak plainer? I am no elegant female, out to plague you. I'm a rational creature, speaking the truth from my heart.

MR. COLLINS [*kneeling with one knee on the settee and leaning over the back of it, toward* ELIZABETH]. You are charming, Miss Elizabeth. Most adorable of creatures, be mine! [*He tries to take her hand.*]

ELIZABETH [*breaking away from him and quickly moving toward the door* D R]. Mr. Collins—please! You are mad—quite mad!

MR. COLLINS. Miss Elizabeth!

[MR. COLLINS *pursues her.* MRS. BENNET *hurries in* D R *just at that moment, a look of eager expectation on her face. She sees what she thinks is a tender scene, and turns away coyly, her hand shielding her eyes, as if not to look.*]

MRS. BENNET [*gayly*]. Congratulations to you both! [*She takes her hand away from her eyes.*] I am overwhelmed with happiness, my dear Mr. Collins. [*She puts a tear in her voice as she moves toward them.*] Lizzy—my darling child——

ELIZABETH [*who has been fuming with anger*]. Spare us your congratulations, Mama. I have declined Mr. Collins' generous offer.

[ELIZABETH *sweeps out* U C, *into the garden.*]

MRS. BENNET [*moving quickly* U C, *looking after her*]. Lizzy! Come back here at once. [*She turns back to* MR. COLLINS *with concern.*] Depend on it, she shall be brought to reason.

MR. COLLINS [*at* C *stage, questioningly*]. She seems very— definite.

MRS. BENNET [*angrily*]. She is a very headstrong, foolish girl!

MR. COLLINS [*perking up at this, and beginning to back down*]. Headstrong? Foolish?

MRS. BENNET. She takes after her father in that respect. But I will bring the stubborn girl to reason.

MR. COLLINS [*edging toward the door* U R]. Stubborn, too? Perhaps—if she has such defects of temper, perhaps it would be better not to force her into accepting me.

MRS. BENNET [*realizing she has gone too far, moving after* MR. COLLINS, *trying to hold him back*]. You misunderstand me! Lizzy is only headstrong in such matters as these. In everything else, she is as sweet-natured a girl as ever lived.

MR. COLLINS [*at the door* U R]. Some other time, my dear Mrs. Bennet.

[MR. COLLINS *bows abruptly and hurries out* U R. MRS. BENNET, *with a wail of dismay, hurries* U L, *and pounds on the door.*]

MRS. BENNET. Mr. Bennet! Mr. Bennet!

[MR. BENNET *comes in* U L.]

MR. BENNET [*impatiently*]. What now?

MRS. BENNET. We are in an uproar! You must make Lizzy marry Mr. Collins.

MR. BENNET [*calmly*]. What are you talking about?

MRS. BENNET [*swinging her hands as she moves to* R C]. Lizzy declares she will not have Mr. Collins, and Mr. Collins begins to say that he will not have Lizzy.

MR. BENNET. Where is Elizabeth?

MRS. BENNET. In the garden.

MR. BENNET [*crossing* U C *and calling off*]. Elizabeth! Come here directly! [*He turns and moves to in front of the settee.*]

MRS. BENNET. Tell her that you insist upon her marrying him.

[ELIZABETH *comes in* U C *and crosses to* C *stage.*]

ELIZABETH. Yes, Father?

MR. BENNET. I understand Mr. Collins has made you an offer of marriage.

ELIZABETH. He has.

MRS. BENNET. I insist upon her accepting it, or I will never see her again. [*She turns away from* ELIZABETH.]

MR. BENNET [*after a short pause*]. An unhappy alternative is before you, Elizabeth. From this day on, you must be a stranger to one of your parents. Your mother will never see you again if you do *not* marry Mr. Collins—and I will never see you again if you *do!*

[MRS. BENNET *whirls about and gasps.* MR. BENNET *starts briskly toward the library* U L. ELIZABETH *smiles with relief.*]

CURTAIN

Act Two—Scene Two

AT RISE OF CURTAIN: *The scene is the same. It is the next afternoon.* MRS. BENNET *is seated on the settee, sewing.* MARY *is seated in the armchair at* L *stage, reading.*]

MRS. BENNET [*plaintively, as the curtain rises*]. I tell you, Mary, nobody takes my part.

MARY [*not looking up*]. Yes, Mama.

MRS. BENNET. I am cruelly used. Nobody feels for my poor nerves.

MARY. Yes, Mama. [*She adds hastily.*] I mean, no, Mama.

MRS. BENNET [*annoyed*]. I thought you, at least, might understand my feelings.

MARY. Yes, Mama.

MRS. BENNET. Mr. Collins has been acting so strangely since he returned from the Lady Lucas' yesterday. I fear that Charlotte is setting her cap for him.

MARY. Charlotte is not artful.

MRS. BENNET [*tartly*]. She is twenty-seven, and must feel quite desperate. Dear me, if my own daughters do not appreciate my efforts——

[ELIZABETH *and* JANE *come in* U R. JANE *carries her needlework.*]

MRS. BENNET. Here she comes now, looking as unconcerned as one may be.

JANE. Please, Mama, don't continue to plague Lizzy.

[JANE *sits down next to* MRS. BENNET *and takes out her needlework.* ELIZABETH *stops at the desk to pick up a book.*]

MRS. BENNET. I tell you, Miss Lizzy, if you take it into your head to go on refusing every offer of marriage in this way, you will never get a husband.

ELIZABETH. Do I seem worried? [*She sits in the armchair* R C *with her book.*]

MRS. BENNET. *I* shall not be able to keep you when your father is dead.

JANE. Don't you think you have talked about it enough? If Lizzy doesn't care for Mr. Collins, then that is the end of it.

MRS. BENNET. I shall never speak of it again. [*And she promptly continues.*] But if Charlotte Lucas marries Mr. Collins, we shan't have a roof over our heads when your poor father dies.

JANE. Please, Mama!

MRS. BENNET [*to* JANE]. At least, I can console myself that *you* have found favor with Mr. Bingley. Do you think he will declare himself soon? I have done everything I can to hurry him along.

[JANE *lowers her head.*]

ELIZABETH. Now, you are embarrassing Jane.

[HILL *comes in* U R *with a note.*]

HILL [*coming to* C]. A note has just been delivered from Netherfield, madam.

MRS. BENNET. For me?

HILL. For Miss Jane.

JANE [*rising and taking the note*]. Thank you, Hill.

[HILL *curtsies and goes out* U R. JANE *stands at* C *stage, opening the note.*]

MRS. BENNET. Read it aloud, Jane.

[JANE *reads the note silently. She seems stricken.*]

MRS. BENNET. From Miss Bingley, I dare say. What elegant paper she uses!

JANE [*quietly*]. It is from Miss Bingley. If you will excuse me—[*She hurries* D R.]—I shall retire to my room.

MRS. BENNET [*disappointed*]. Without reading the note?

ELIZABETH [*anxiously, rising*]. Jane, is it bad news?

JANE [*hesitating*]. It is—surprising news.

MRS. BENNET [*gaily*]. A surprise! Come, tell us!

JANE [*taking a deep breath*]. The Bingleys have taken leave of Netherfield and are on their way to town.

ELIZABETH [*surprised*]. They have *gone?*

JANE. Without any intention of coming back again. Mr. Darcy is remaining to close the house for his friend.

MRS. BENNET. I can't believe it!

JANE [*glancing at the note again*]. It seems to have been a very—sudden decision.

MRS. BENNET. Mr. Bingley *said* he makes up his mind in a hurry—but—no! Jane, it can't be true.

ELIZABETH [*hotly, moving to* C]. It's all Mr. Darcy's doing. I'll warrant.

MARY. But why should *he* interfere?

ELIZABETH. If your nose wasn't always buried in a book, you'd realize how proud he is. He considers our Jane not rich or grand enough for Mr. Bingley.

MRS. BENNET [*with a shudder*]. That odious Mr. Darcy!

JANE. Caroline says she hopes we may meet again at some future time, and regrets that they could not call to bid me farewell.

ELIZABETH. Oh, *does* she?

JANE [*her voice breaking*]. She hints there is an attachment between Mr. Bingley and Mr. Darcy's young sister.

ELIZABETH. I don't believe it! No one who has seen you two together can doubt his affection for *you*. That, too, is Mr. Darcy's plan—to wed his sister to Mr. Bingley.

MRS. BENNET [*crossing* D R, *putting her arm around* JANE]. My poor, dear Jane. Come to your room and I will put cold compresses on your forehead.

JANE [*breaking away*]. Please, Mama, I'd rather be alone.

[*With a sob,* JANE *hurries out* D R.]

MARY [*following her*]. Perhaps I can console her with some of my extracts.

[MARY *goes out* D R.]

ELIZABETH [*pacing to the fireplace*]. Believe me, Mr. Darcy is at the back of this.

MRS. BENNET [*coming to* C]. He wouldn't dare!

ELIZABETH [*moving to left of the settee*]. He has. He and Miss Bingley between them.

[LYDIA *and* CATHERINE *hurry in* U R. LYDIA *is jubilant, but* CATHERINE *is on the verge of tears*.]

LYDIA [*excitedly, coming to* MRS. BENNET]. Mama, the most exciting thing!

CATHERINE [*tearfully, following her*]. The regiment has been ordered to Brighton!

ELIZABETH. At last one may take a walk to Meryton without stumbling over an officer. [*She sits in the armchair at* L *stage.*]

CATHERINE. How *can* you joke about it? [*She flings herself down in the armchair* R C *and buries her head in her arms.*]

MRS. BENNET [*crossing to her and patting her shoulder*]. Poor little Kitty! Well do I remember how I cried for two days when Colonel Miller's regiment went away. My heart was broken. [*She sighs.*]

ELIZABETH. How is it that *you* are so cheerful, Lydia?
CATHERINE [*sobbing*]. *She* has nothing to cry about!

[LYDIA *has been doing a gay little dance step at* C *stage.*]

MRS. BENNET. There—now. If only your papa would let us all go to Brighton for the summer!

ELIZABETH. Papa would never agree. [*She rises.*] Come, Lydia, out with the news you're bursting with.

LYDIA [*triumphantly*]. Colonel Forster's wife has invited *me* to go with her on a visit!

MRS. BENNET [*pleased*]. Why, Lydia! Has she, really!

LYDIA [*happily*]. She said a little sea air is just what I needed.

CATHERINE [*wailing*]. It would do *me* a great deal of good, too.

LYDIA [*unsympathetically*]. But it was *me* she invited. [*She continues rapturously, moving* D R *with a giddy whirl.*]

CATHERINE. I can't see why Mrs. Forster shouldn't ask *me* as well as Lydia. I'm two years older.

LYDIA [*taking* CATHERINE *by the arm*]. Come, dry your eyes and help me look over my clothes. I shall need at least two new bonnets. [*She pulls* CATHERINE D R.]

CATHERINE [*drying her eyes*]. Nobody ever asks *me* anywhere.

MRS. BENNET [*her good spirits returning*]. Your new blue will be elegant for balls, Lydia. We must put a little more lace on it.

[MRS. BENNET *crosses* D R, *to* LYDIA *and* CATHERINE. MR. BENNET *comes in* U L.]

MR. BENNET [*moving above the settee to* C *stage*]. What is all the to-do about this time?

CATHERINE [*wailing again*]. The regiment has been ordered to Brighton!

MRS. BENNET. And Mrs. Forster has invited Lydia to visit her awhile!

LYDIA [*taking* MRS. BENNET'S *arm*]. I must have just yards and yards of lace.

[MRS. BENNET, LYDIA, *and* CATHERINE *go out* D R, CATHERINE *still sniffling.*]

MR. BENNET [*dryly*]. I don't remember hearing anyone ask *my* permission for this trip. [*He sits on the settee.*]

ELIZABETH [*going over to him*]. Please, Papa. Don't let her go.

MR. BENNET. Why not?

ELIZABETH. Mrs. Forster is so young for a chaperone, and there will be so many officers at Brighton.

MR. BENNET. Lydia will never be happy until she has made a spectacle of herself in some place or other, and we can never expect her to do it with so little expense or inconvenience to her family as under the present circumstances.

ELIZABETH [*sitting on the settee*]. But her manner is so unguarded and imprudent!

MR. BENNET [*patting her hand*]. I think you exaggerate, my dear. Foolish, she undoubtedly is, but scarcely out of hand.

ELIZABETH. She is already a determined little flirt. Oh, Papa, I am asking this for her own good.

MR. BENNET. We shall have no peace at Longbourn if she doesn't go. Colonel Forster is a sensible man, and will keep her out of any real mischief.

ELIZABETH. I sincerely hope so.

MR. BENNET [*rising*]. I'll give her my consent, so that she won't disturb me by asking for it later.

[MR. BENNET *goes out* D R. ELIZABETH *rises and starts to* C. *She hears voices off* U C *and hurries to the door.*]

ELIZABETH [*surprised*]. Charlotte—and *Mr. Collins!* What are you doing in the garden?

[CHARLOTTE *and* MR. COLLINS *come in* U C. CHARLOTTE *appears happy enough.* MR. COLLINS *looks very smug. They come to* C *with* ELIZABETH.]

MR. COLLINS. Miss Charlotte kindly consented to return with me. I have been calling on Sir William and Lady Lucas.

CHARLOTTE. I have something very important to tell you, Eliza.

ELIZABETH. I hope it's good news. We have had so much of the other kind.

MR. COLLINS. May I speak with Mr. Bennet?

ELIZABETH. Papa went out that way a minute ago. [*She points* D R.]

MR. COLLINS. Thank you.

[MR. COLLINS *bows and goes out* D R.]

ELIZABETH [*bringing* CHARLOTTE *over to the settee and sitting*]. How kind of you, Charlotte, to pass a little time with Mr. Collins. It keeps him in a good humor, and I'm more obliged to you than I can say.

CHARLOTTE. Why should I not? Mr. Collins and I are engaged to be married.

ELIZABETH [*unbelievingly*]. Engaged to Mr. Collins! Charlotte —impossible!

CHARLOTTE [*calmly*]. Not at all.

ELIZABETH [*embarrassed*]. I'm—I'm sorry. I didn't mean that. I wish you every happiness.

CHARLOTTE [*humbly*]. I'm not unaware, Lizzy, that Mr. Collins asked you first to marry him.

ELIZABETH [*pressing her arm tenderly*]. Dear Charlotte. He only did it out of—duty, I'm sure.

CHARLOTTE. I'm not romantic, you know. I asked only a comfortable home, and I'm convinced that my chance of happiness with Mr. Collins is as good as most people can hope for.

ELIZABETH. Of course. [*Then, she speaks with emotion.*] Oh, Charlotte, I sincerely *do* hope you will be happy! [*She puts her arms around* CHARLOTTE *and kisses her.*]

CHARLOTTE. Will you come and visit me after I am married?

[ELIZABETH *rises and turns away* D L, *without answering.* CHARLOTTE *follows her and speaks insistently.*]

CHARLOTTE. Promise me, Elizabeth.

ELIZABETH [*reluctantly*]. I promise.

CHARLOTTE. Thank you. [*She goes* D R *with* ELIZABETH.] I must hear how your mother takes the news!

[CHARLOTTE *goes out* D R, *leaving* ELIZABETH D R. ELIZABETH *looks after her and shakes her head.*]

LYDIA [*off* D R]. Charlotte! How nice to see you!

[LYDIA *comes in* D R. *She has her bonnet on, and carries her parasol. She crosses to* C *stage.*]

LYDIA [*preening*]. This bonnet is quite passable, but Mama and I are going shopping for more, and some new gowns. She has persuaded Jane to come along. [*She dances toward the door* U C.] Tell them I'll be waiting out here.

[LYDIA *goes out* U C. ELIZABETH *moves toward the fireplace.* JANE *comes in* D R. *She carries her bonnet.*]

ELIZABETH [*looking up*]. Lydia tells me you are going shopping.

JANE [*moving agitatedly to* C]. I *must* do something.

ELIZABETH. You know how I feel for you.

JANE. Mama is determined now that I pay a visit to Aunt Gardiner in London.

ELIZABETH. Why don't you? [*She sits on the settee.*] The change would do you a world of good.

JANE. But Mama's plan is that I should write to Caroline Bingley from there, and then she and her brother would call on me.

ELIZABETH [*dryly*]. How like Mama!

JANE [*crossing quickly to* ELIZABETH, *flinging herself down on the settee, and burying her head on* ELIZABETH'S *shoulder*]. Oh, Lizzy, what shall I do? My heart is broken.

[JANE'S *voice breaks, and she sobs heartbrokenly.* ELIZABETH *lifts up her head and strokes her face.*]

ELIZABETH. Dear Jane!

JANE [*freeing herself, and trying to speak firmly*]. I'll forget him soon, and we'll all be as we were before.

[ELIZABETH *looks at her but says nothing.*]

JANE. You doubt me. [*She rises and moves to* C.] Indeed, you have no reason. He may live in my memory, but—that is all.

ELIZABETH [*spiritedly, rising, crossing to her, putting her arm about her*]. Dear Jane, you're too good! I don't know what to say to you. I feel as if I've never done you justice, or loved you as you deserve.

JANE. Oh, no!

ELIZABETH. *You* wish to think all the world as good as you are. But the more I see of the world, the more I am dissatisfied with it. And now, Charlotte's engagement. [*She crosses* D L.] It's unaccountable!

JANE. No, Lizzy. Remember that Charlotte is one of a large family, but little fortune. She may feel something like regard and esteem for our cousin.

ELIZABETH. I can't bring myself to think so. Mr. Collins is a conceited, pompous, narrow-minded, silly man, and Charlotte knows that as well as we do.

[MRS. BENNET *and* MR. BENNET *come in* D R. MRS. BENNET *is dressed for her shopping trip.* MR. BENNET *pauses at* R C.]

MRS. BENNET [*as she comes in and moves to* JANE]. Indeed, Mr. Bennet, it is very hard to think that Charlotte Lucas should ever be mistress of this house!

ELIZABETH [*wearily*]. Lydia is waiting in the garden, Mama.

MRS. BENNET. Come, Jane.

[MRS. BENNET *goes* U C, *followed by* JANE.]

MRS. BENNET [*pausing* U C]. *I'll* be forced to make way for Charlotte Lucas, and live to see her take my place here!

MR. BENNET. My dear, don't give way to such gloomy thoughts. Let us hope for better things. Let us flatter ourselves that *I* may outlive you.

[MRS. BENNET *gives him an outraged look. Then, taking* JANE'S *arm, she flounces out* U C.]

MR. BENNET [*cheerfully, crossing to* C *stage*]. So, Lizzy, your sister Jane is crossed in love, I find.

ELIZABETH [*annoyed*]. Papa, don't you take anything seriously? [*She sits on the bench.*]

MR. BENNET. I discovered long ago that the only way for a mere man to survive in a household of women is to see the amusing side of everything.

ELIZABETH. You're *not* laughing at Jane!

MR. BENNET [*soberly, moving to* L C]. No, my dear, I am not. [*He continues more cheerfully.*] But it is a comfort to think that whatever may befall any of you, you have an affectionate mother who will always make the most of it.

[HILL *comes in* U R *as* MR. BENNET *goes out* U L.]

HILL [*coming to* C]. Mr. Fitzwilliam Darcy.

ELIZABETH [*starting*]. Oh! [*She rises.*] Why—tell him to come in.

HILL. Yes, Miss Elizabeth.

[HILL *curtsies and goes out* U R. *In a moment, she returns to usher in* MR. DARCY, *who comes to* C. *For the first time, he appears ill at ease.* HILL *goes out* U R *again.*]

ELIZABETH [*coldly*]. Good afternoon.

MR. DARCY [*bowing*]. I am glad to find you alone, Miss Elizabeth.

ELIZABETH. Indeed! Your friends left Netherfield quite suddenly, Mr. Darcy.

MR. DARCY. I have seen to the closing of the house for them.

ELIZABETH [*sitting on the settee again*]. I understand that Mr. Bingley is not likely to return again.

MR. DARCY [*sitting stiffly in the armchair* R C]. It is probable that he may spend very little of his time there in the future.

ELIZABETH. Indeed!

[*There is a painful silence.* MR. DARCY *gets up abruptly and walks* U C. ELIZABETH *watches him in puzzled surprise. He is silent for a few moments; then he comes toward her.*]

MR. DARCY [*agitatedly*]. I have struggled in vain. It will not do. My feelings won't be repressed. You must allow me to tell you how ardently I admire and love you.

ELIZABETH [*astonished*]. Mr. Darcy!

MR. DARCY. My attachment is so strong that in spite of all my endeavors, I find it impossible to conquer my feelings for you.

ELIZABETH [*in mingled resentment and surprise*]. You mean you have tried *not* to love me, Mr. Darcy?

MR. DARCY. I realize that there is a great difference in our connections, and that there are great disadvantages in marrying into such a family as yours, but none the less I hope you may accept my hand!

ELIZABETH [*angrily, rising*]. How dare you speak of my family in that way?

MR. DARCY [*crossing close to her*]. It is because I love you, Miss Elizabeth, that I dare speak at all—that I dare to offend the society of which I am a part.

ELIZABETH. You are insufferable, Mr. Darcy, to speak of love and offense in the same breath. [*She moves past him to in front of the armchair* R C.]

MR. DARCY [*angrily, but with forced calmness*]. And this is all the reply which I may expect?

ELIZABETH [*her back to him*]. It is more than you deserve. [*She whirls to face him.*] Do you think I would marry any man who liked me against his will and against his reason? Do you think any consideration would tempt me to accept the man who has been the means of ruining the happiness of my sister?

MR. DARCY. I do not understand you.

ELIZABETH. You *dare not* understand me! Can you deny that you have been the means of separating Jane and Mr. Bingley?

MR. DARCY [*stiffly*]. I?

ELIZABETH [*crossing directly to him*]. Can you deny that you have done it?

MR. DARCY [*after a short pause, in which he faces front*]. I have no wish to deny that I did everything in my power to separate Mr. Bingley from your sister. Toward *him* I have been kinder than toward myself.

ELIZABETH. Oh! They love each other, Mr. Darcy. What right have you to take their happiness in your hands? You speak of love. What can you know of love?

MR. DARCY [*turning to face her*]. And is this your opinion of me?

ELIZABETH. It is. [*She moves to* R C.]

MR. DARCY [*bowing*]. I thank you for explaining so fully. My faults, according to this calculation, are heavy indeed.

ELIZABETH [*facing front*]. They are.

MR. DARCY. But perhaps these offenses might have been overlooked, had not your pride been hurt.

ELIZABETH [*turning to him, sharply*]. *My* pride?

MR. DARCY [*crossing to her*]. Was it not pride that prohibited you from accepting my honest confession of the reasons why I could not ask you sooner to be my wife?

ELIZABETH [*furiously*]. You could not have made me the offer of your hand in any *possible* way that would have tempted me to accept it!

[MR. DARCY *looks at her with mingled incredulity and mortification.*]

ELIZABETH [*continuing, moving to in front of the settee*]. You are the last man in the world whom I could ever be prevailed upon to marry! It is not alone your unfeeling disregard of Jane's happiness. I know you also to be false to the obligations which family loyalty impose on you.

MR. DARCY [*after a moment's puzzled pause*]. You refer, perhaps, to Mr. Wickham?

ELIZABETH. I do.

MR. DARCY. Then forgive me for having taken up so much of your time, and accept my best wishes for your happiness!

[MR. DARCY *bows stiffly and goes out* U R. ELIZABETH *stands looking after him a moment. Then she sinks down on the settee and buries her face in her arms.*]

CURTAIN

Act Three—Scene One

AT RISE OF CURTAIN: *The scene is the same. It is an after-noon in July.* MARY *is sitting in the armchair by the fireplace, reading.* CATHERINE *is standing* U C, *near the glass doors to the garden. With* LYDIA *gone,* CATHERINE *is bored, and in-clined to be fretful and peevish.*]

CATHERINE [*looking out*]. Why doesn't she come?

MARY. It seems an age since Lizzy went to Charlotte's.

CATHERINE [*coming to* C]. Six whole weeks! Imagine having to listen to Mr. Collins that long!

MARY. In my opinion, Mr. Collins has some very erudite thoughts.

CATHERINE. Mama will never quite forgive Lizzy for not marrying him.

MARY [*stiffly*]. Marriage is not the only end in life.

CATHERINE [*sitting in the armchair at* R C]. It's the best begin-ning that I know of. [*She sighs.*] I wish I were at Brighton with Lydia.

MARY. Lydia is turning out to be a silly, empty-headed flirt.

CATHERINE. But what a time she must be having! Mr. Wick-ham is escorting her to all the balls. [*She speaks sadly as she rises and crosses to the doors* U C *again to glance out.*] And all *I* do is watch for other people to come home .

[MRS. BENNET *and* JANE *come in* D R. JANE *looks pale and tired and listless.* MRS. BENNET *is fussing over her like a hen with one chick.*]

MRS. BENNET [*moving toward the settee*]. Now, my dear, just relax on the settee for a few minutes. You must not exert yourself.

JANE. Mama, I am *not* an invalid! [*She sits on the settee.*]

MRS. BENNET [*pausing right of the settee*]. There is not a spot of color in your cheeks since you came back from London. I don't know what your Aunt Gardiner was thinking of, to let you get so run down. [*She moves behind the settee and props a pillow behind* JANE'S *back.*]

JANE. Aunt Gardiner was very kind. And I feel perfectly fit. Really, I do. [*But she leans back on the pillow gratefully.*]

MARY [*rising*]. Men—as some wise person once observed—are at the bottom of all our trouble. [*She pauses thoughtfully.*] Or did he say women?

MRS. BENNET. Has the postman come, Kitty? It's quite some time since I've had a letter from Lydia.

CATHERINE. Lydia was very well, Mama, according to *my* last letter. [*She glances out* U C *excitedly.*] Here comes Papa's carriage now!

MARY [*closing her book reluctantly*]. I will get no more reading done this afternoon.

MRS. BENNET. No doubt Lizzy has told your father all the news before we even get a whisper of it.

CATHERINE [*coming down to* MRS. BENNET]. There can't be much news from a visit to Mr. and Mrs. Collins.

[ELIZABETH *hurries in* U R, *followed by* MR. BENNET.]

ELIZABETH [*coming to* C]. Mama! [*She kisses* MRS. BENNET.] And dear Jane! And Kitty and Mary. [*She smiles at them all.*] How good it is to be home again!

MR. BENNET [*who has followed her to* C]. I'm glad you have come back, Lizzy.

MRS. BENNET. Dear me, so are we all. You must tell us the news.

CATHERINE. How does Charlotte look? Does she seem happy?

ELIZABETH [*sitting on the settee with* JANE]. Let me get my breath first.

MR. BENNET. The presence of a mere man may not still the clatter of female tongues, but I think you will talk more freely without me.

[MR. BENNET *goes out* U R. CATHERINE *sits on the bench* D L, *while* MRS. BENNET *sits in the armchair at* R C. MARY *resumes her seat.*]

ELIZABETH [*studying* JANE]. Jane, you look tired.

JANE [*quickly*]. It's nothing. I had a most delightful time in London.

ELIZABETH [*bluntly*]. Did Mr. Bingley call to see you?

JANE [*embarrassed*]. He was—he was very busy. His sister Caroline called.

MRS. BENNET [*bluntly*]. Once. One fifteen-minute call.

JANE [*striving to speak cheerfully*]. But it's *your* news that we are anxious to hear.

CATHERINE. Did you see any good-looking men to flirt with?

ELIZABETH. Charlotte seems quite happy, and they live very comfortably.

MRS. BENNET. Well, I only hope it will last. What sort of table do they keep? Charlotte is an excellent manager, I dare say.

ELIZABETH. She is.

MRS. BENNET. I suppose they often talk of having Longbourn when your father is dead.

ELIZABETH. They never mentioned it before me.

JANE. Need we go into that again, Mama?

MRS. BENNET. I'll not say another word. [*She rises and moves to* C.] Besides, we have taxed you long enough, Jane. It's time you were out in the sun for a little while.

JANE. I much prefer to remain in here and talk with Lizzy.

MRS. BENNET. Nonsense! You must get a little color back in your cheeks.

ELIZABETH. You're quite right, Mama.

MRS. BENNET. Kitty, go to your room with Mary and see if you can do a little studying. I shall see to Jane's chair.

[MRS. BENNET *goes out* U C.]

MARY [*rising*]. Yes, Mama.

[MARY *and* CATHERINE *go out* D R.]

JANE [*eagerly*]. Lizzy, tell me everything. Did you see Mr. Darcy?

ELIZABETH. I saw him quite often. At Lady Catherine's.

JANE. Did he make any reference to that *strange* proposal of his?

ELIZABETH. None at all, but he seemed to put himself out to be more agreeable.

JANE. Oh, Lizzy—do you really think you did right?

ELIZABETH [*rising, moving up right of the settee to behind it*]. You don't *blame* me for refusing him?

JANE. Oh, no! But to be thwarted in love is a terrible thing. [*She lowers her head, and there is a catch in her voice.*]

ELIZABETH [*stroking her hair*]. Dear Jane—always thinking of someone else. Tell me about your trip to London.

JANE. Caroline called only once. I confess I've been entirely deceived in her regard for me.

ELIZABETH. I suspected as much. [*She moves toward the fireplace.*]

JANE. She mentioned that Mr. Bingley was partial to Miss Darcy, and that they expected the announcement any day.

ELIZABETH. It can't be true! He loved you, Jane. I'm sure of it.

JANE. I am quite resigned to it now. [*There is a pause.*] At least, I try to be. [*Her voice breaks.*] But I still love him,

Lizzy—I can't help it. [*She puts her head down on the back of the settee and sobs.*]

[ELIZABETH *hurries to behind the settee and strokes* JANE'S *head, comfortingly.* MRS. BENNET *comes in* U C.]

MRS. BENNET [*coming down to right of the settee*]. I've moved your chair into the sun, and Hill has fixed it with pillows. Come, now, Jane.

JANE [*rising*]. Yes, Mama.

MRS. BENNET. Bring that light woolen shawl for your shoulders. There might be a little draught.

JANE [*looking on the settee for the shawl*]. I left it upstairs. [*She starts* D R.]

MRS. BENNET. Lizzy will get it for you.

JANE. Mama, I will *not* be treated as an invalid!

[JANE *goes out* D R.]

MRS. BENNET [*sighing*]. Well, Lizzy, what is your opinion now of this sad business of Jane's?

ELIZABETH. I'm worried about her health. [*She moves toward the fireplace.*]

MRS. BENNET [*sitting on the settee*]. For my part, I'm determined never again to speak of Mr. Bingley to anyone. He is a very undeserving young man, and I don't suppose there's the least chance in the world of her ever getting him now.

ELIZABETH. I think not.

MRS. BENNET. I'm sure poor Jane will die of a broken heart, and then he will be sorry for what he has done.

[HILL *comes in* U R.]

HILL. Lady Lucas, madam.

MRS. BENNET. Very well, Hill.

[HILL *curtsies and goes out* U R.]

MRS. BENNET [*rising, moving to* C]. She has come to boast again about Charlotte's marriage!

ELIZABETH. She probably wants to hear if Charlotte is well.

MRS. BENNET. Every time she calls, I can see her looking the place over, and I know she is wondering just when Mr. Bennet is going to die—so that Charlotte can move in.

[LADY LUCAS *comes in* U R *and moves to* C. MRS. BENNET'S *tone changes quickly.*]

MRS. BENNET [*effusively*]. My dear Lady Lucas! [*She kisses her.*]

[ELIZABETH *curtsies.*]

LADY LUCAS [*crossing past* MRS. BENNET *to the settee*]. I'm glad to see you home again, Elizabeth. How did you leave my dear Charlotte and her good husband? [*She sits on the settee.*]

ELIZABETH [*sitting on the bench* D L]. In the best of health. They sent their kindest regards.

LADY LUCAS [*sweetly, to* MRS. BENNET, *who is standing at* C]. It is such a comfort, having a daughter well married. You can't know how happy I am!

MRS. BENNET [*annoyed, moving a few steps* D C]. What *is* keeping Jane?

LADY LUCAS. What a pity that young Mr. Bingley doesn't return! Lydia is enjoying herself at Brighton, I trust?

MRS. BENNET. Indeed, yes.

[JANE *comes in* D R *with the shawl. She moves to* R C *and curtsies to* LADY LUCAS.]

JANE. How nice to see you, Lady Lucas.

LADY LUCAS. Jane! You're looking so pale!

MRS. BENNET [*quickly, leading* JANE *to the armchair* R C, *and seating her*]. It's nothing—a slight indisposition.

LADY LUCAS. I hope Lydia is not seeing too much of Mr. Wickham at Brighton. I hear that he left gaming debts of considerable amount behind him in Meryton.

ELIZABETH [*surprised*]. Gaming debts!

LADY LUCAS. His pleasant countenance seems to have deceived a great many people. They say he is in debt to every tradesman in the place.

ELIZABETH. Can this be true? I had no idea of it!

MRS. BENNET. Dear me! Neither had I. [*She sits on the settee.*]

LADY LUCAS. People in Meryton are all turned against him now, though there was a time when they all considered Mr. Wickham ill-used by Mr. Darcy.

ELIZABETH [*surprised*]. Do you mean he has told it generally that Mr. Darcy cheated him out of his inheritance?

LADY LUCAS. My dear, everyone knows about it.

ELIZABETH [*rising, perturbed, and turning toward the fireplace*]. But I thought—he said not for the world would he injure Mr. Darcy's reputation.

LADY LUCAS. It seems that was exactly the method he used *to* ruin it.

JANE. Mr. Wickham's deceived us, Lizzy!

LADY LUCAS. I have it on good authority that Mr. Darcy refused to give him a living in the church only because of his unreliable character.

MRS. BENNET. Oh!

ELIZABETH. I can scarcely believe it!

LADY LUCAS [*pleased at having created a mild sensation*]. I assure you it is the truth.

[LADY LUCAS *rises, and* MRS. BENNET *and* JANE *rise, also.*
JANE *moves to* C *stage.*]

LADY LUCAS [*to* ELIZABETH]. Thank you for your kind mes-
sages from Charlotte.

ELIZABETH. You are most welcome.

LADY LUCAS [*crossing* U R]. Walk with me to my carriage, Mrs.
Bennet. A little fresh air may do you good.

MRS. BENNET. Dear me—yes! My nerves are all aflutter.

[MRS. BENNET *and* LADY LUCAS *go out* U R.]

ELIZABETH [*contritely, moving to* JANE]. Jane, how *could* I
have accused Mr. Darcy of injustice to Mr. Wickham when
I didn't know the facts!

JANE. We were so wrong about him, Lizzy. I'm ashamed. [*She
sits in the armchair* R C *again.*]

ELIZABETH. I, who prided myself on being such a clever judge
of character!

JANE. *Lizzy*, if I didn't know that you dislike him so much, I
would almost say—[*She pauses, and then looks up at her.*]
—that you are in love with him!

ELIZABETH [*startled*]. In love with Mr. Darcy? Never! [*She
moves over to the fireplace.*]

JANE [*gently*]. It is possible to deceive one's heart for a little
while. [*She rises, putting the shawl about her shoulders.*]

ELIZABETH. He separated you from Mr. Bingley. I will never
forgive him that.

JANE. Mama will be upset if I don't go outside. [*She crosses
to* ELIZABETH.] I didn't mean to offend you, Lizzy.

ELIZABETH [*holding her close to her for a moment*]. You could
never do that, dear Jane. [*She crosses* U C *with* JANE.]

[JANE *goes out* U C. ELIABETH *moves* D L *and stares thoughtfully into the fireplace.* MRS. BENNET *comes in* U R *and
crosses to the settee.*]

MRS. BENNET. Did you notice how Lady Lucas looked at the settee? No doubt she plans to advise Charlotte to recover it.

ELIZABETH. You imagine things, Mama.

[MR. BENNET *comes in* U R, *rather excitedly. He has a letter in his hand.*]

MR. BENNET [*in a serious tone, coming to* C]. Before your nerves give way over trifles, madam, I have some news of real import. [*He indicates the letter.*] An express from Colonel Forster in Brighton.

MRS. BENNET [*excitedly*]. About Lydia?

MR. BENNET. She has gone off with Mr. Wickham.

MRS. BENNET. Lydia married! Oh, how happy I am! [*She hugs* ELIZABETH.]

MR. BENNET. Wait, my dear. From a note that Lydia left, it is evident that she *expected* to be married at once. But from what Colonel Forster has been able to find out, no marriage has taken place.

MRS. BENNET [*shrilly*]. No marriage!

[MRS. BENNET *screams and puts her hand to her head.* ELIZA-BETH *puts her arm around her.*]

ELIZABETH. Mama!

[JANE *comes hurrying in* U C, *alarmed.*]

JANE [*coming to* C]. What is it?

ELIZABETH. Lydia has eloped with Mr. Wickham, but he seems to have no intention of marrying her.

JANE. Oh, poor Lydia! And poor *Mama!* [*She goes to* MRS. BENNET *and also puts an arm about her.*]

MR. BENNET. Colonel Forster believes they were headed for London. I will start for there at once. Your Uncle Gardiner may be able to help me trace them.

[MR. BENNET *hurries out* U R.]

MRS. BENNET [*sinking down on the settee*]. That villainous Wickham! [*She breaks into sobs.*]

[JANE *and* ELIZABETH *sit beside her, comforting* MRS. BENNET.]

JANE [*anxiously*]. Don't cry, Mama, please.
MRS. BENNET. Why did the Forsters let her out of their sight?
ELIZABETH. No one could watch Lydia *all* the time.

[HILL *comes in* U R *and waits tentatively* U C.]

MRS. BENNET [*on a wailing crescendo*]. And now here's Mr. Bennet going away, and I know he will fight Mr. Wickham, and then he will be killed, and we shall be turned out, and all because you would not marry Mr. Collins!
ELIZABETH. Please, Mama!
JANE. Come, you must lie down in your room.

[JANE *and* ELIZABETH *help* MRS. BENNET *to her feet. They start* D R *with her.*]

MRS. BENNET [*lamenting*]. The Collinses will turn us out of here before your father is cold in his grave!
ELIZABETH. Please, Mama!

[JANE *and* MRS. BENNET *go out* D R. ELIZABETH *is about to follow when* HILL *comes quickly* D C.]

HILL. Miss Elizabeth.

[ELIZABETH *turns in the doorway* D R.]

HILL. Mr. Darcy is here to see you.
ELIZABETH [*distressed*]. Mr. Darcy? [*She pauses.*] Show—show him in.

[HILL *curtsies and goes out* U R. ELIZABETH *crosses nervously to the settee and sits, her head down, twisting her hands.* MR. DARCY *comes in* U R.]

MR. DARCY [*coming to* C *and bowing low*]. Miss Elizabeth.

ELIZABETH [*in a low voice*]. How-do-you-do, Mr. Darcy. I'm surprised to see you.

MR. DARCY. You would not also be a little—"happy"—to see me, Miss Elizabeth?

ELIZABETH [*taken aback*]. "Happy"? Oh, Mr. Darcy, I find it hard to be "happy"——[*Her voice breaks on the last word, and she bows her head.*]

MR. DARCY [*concerned, crossing closer to the settee*]. What is the matter, Miss Elizabeth?

ELIZABETH [*looking up*]. Oh, Mr. Darcy!

MR. DARCY. Shall I get you a glass of wine?

ELIZABETH [*striving for calmness*]. Please! There is nothing the matter. I am only distressed by some dreadful news. [*She turns away, with a little sob.*]

MR. DARCY. Try to calm yourself, Miss Elizabeth. I was riding back to London after my visit to Lady Catherine. How fortunate it is that I stopped in here. [*He sits beside her.*]

ELIZABETH [*pleased at his concern, in spite of her tears*]. Is it? [*She dries her tears, sniffing daintily now and then.*]

MR. DARCY. If you will let me be of some service to you.

ELIZABETH [*looking up*]. No one can do much for us now! My youngest sister has eloped—has thrown herself into the power of—of Mr. Wickham. You know him too well to doubt the rest.

MR. DARCY [*rising*]. Wickham!

ELIZABETH. She has no money, no connections, nothing that can tempt him to marry her.

MR. DARCY. Now you know his true character? [*He moves to* c.]

ELIZABETH [*abjectly*]. Yes. Oh, Mr. Darcy, how we have wronged you in regard to him.

MR. DARCY. I am grieved—shocked. [*He turns back to her.*] But is it certain—absolutely certain?

ELIZABETH [*nodding*]. Yes.

MR. DARCY. And what is being done to recover her?

ELIZABETH. My father is going to London. But nothing can be done. We are in disgrace. [*She sobs again.*]

MR. DARCY. Control your tears—please, Miss Elizabeth. [*He moves toward her, as if to comfort her.*]

ELIZABETH. Such humiliation! No one will speak to us again. [*She looks up hopefully at him.*]

MR. DARCY [*sitting beside her*]. I wish that I could say or do something to ease you in your distress.

ELIZABETH. Lydia is lost forever!

MR. DARCY [*taking her hand*]. Don't give up all hope, Miss Elizabeth. [*He rises.*] Now—I must ask you to excuse me.

ELIZABETH [*disappointed*]. You're going? [*She rises.*]

MR. DARCY. To London—immediately.

ELIZABETH. Will you ever forgive me, Mr. Darcy, for thinking ill of you?

MR. DARCY [*with a touch of humor*]. I will try.

[MR. DARCY *bends and kisses her hand, lingeringly. Then he bows and goes out* U R. ELIZABETH *glances after him, and then at her hand, which is still extended. She gives a little smile and brings her hand up to her cheek.*]

ELIZABETH. Oh—Darcy—Darcy!

CURTAIN

Act Three—Scene Two

AT RISE OF CURTAIN: *The scene is the same. It is morning, a week later.* MR. BENNET *is standing near the fireplace, lighting his pipe.* ELIZABETH *comes in* U R *and moves to* L C. *She carries a piece of needlework.*]

MR. BENNET. Is your mother any better this morning?

ELIZABETH. Very little. She declares over and over again that her heart is broken.

MR. BENNET. I blame myself for this. But I could find no trace of Lydia or Wickham in London.

ELIZABETH [*sitting in the armchair at* L *stage, doing her needlework*]. You mustn't be too severe on yourself, Papa.

MR. BENNET. No, Lizzy, for once in my life let me feel that I have been to blame. I should have taken your advice and never let Lydia go to Brighton.

ELIZABETH. It's too late for that now.

[CATHERINE *comes in* U R.]

CATHERINE [*coming* R C]. Jane has persuaded Mama to come downstairs for a little while.

ELIZABETH. Is she dressing?

CATHERINE. Yes—although she declares she is too weak to stand.

MR. BENNET. Your mother knows how to give such elegance to misfortune. Next time I may do the same—perhaps when Kitty runs away.

CATHERINE [*peevishly, sitting in the armchair* R C]. I'm not going to run away, Papa. If *I* should go to Brighton, I would behave better than Lydia.

MR. BENNET [*crossing to her*]. *You* go to Brighton! No, Kitty. I have at least learned to be cautious, and you will feel the effects of it.

[CATHERINE *takes out her handkerchief and begins to dab at her eyes.*]

MR. BENNET [*patting her shoulder*]. Well, well, do not make yourself unhappy. If you are a good girl for the next ten years, I may take you to the theatre at the end of them.

[CATHERINE *bursts into tears and runs out* D R. MRS. BENNET *is heard off* U R, *wailing.*]

JANE [*off* U R]. Now, Mama, don't hurry.

[MR. BENNET *glances* U R *and then makes a hurried exit* U L. MRS. BENNET *and* JANE *come in* U R. MRS. BENNET *looks as stricken as possible and leans heavily on* JANE.]

MRS. BENNET [*walking slowly to the settee with* JANE]. What a dreadful state I am in! Such tremblings, such flutterings all over me!

[*With* JANE'S *help*, MRS. BENNET *relaxes on the settee*. JANE *hovers near her, adjusting the pillows*. MARY *comes in* D R.]

ELIZABETH. You must try to think of something else, Mama.

MRS. BENNET [*feeling the afflicted areas*]. Such spasms in my side and pains in my head—such beatings at my heart—that I can get no rest night or day.

MARY. Kitty is in tears.

ELIZABETH [*dryly*]. We shall all float away if there are any more tears shed.

MARY [*sitting in the armchair at* R C]. This is a most unfortunate affair and will probably be much talked of.

MRS. BENNET [*wailing*]. Oh, Lydia, Lydia!

MARY [*oratorically*]. We must stem the tide of malice, and pour into the wounded bosoms of each other the balm of sisterly consolation.

[*This makes* MRS. BENNET *sob anew.*]

JANE [*comforting her, as she sits right of her*]. Now, Mama!

MARY. Unhappy as the event must be for Lydia, we must not shrink from the useful lesson that loss of virtue in a female is irretrievable.

[MRS. BENNET *sobs loudly.* ELIZABETH *rises, crosses above the settee, and over to* MARY. *She takes* MARY *by the shoulders and propels her toward* U C.]

ELIZABETH. You had better get some fresh air!

MARY [*as she is propelled along*]. A woman's reputation is no less brittle than it is beautiful.

ELIZABETH [*loudly*]. And please keep quiet!

MARY [*as she goes out*]. She cannot be too guarded in her behavior toward the undeserving sex.

[ELIZABETH *gives her a decided push.*]

MARY [*outraged*]. Ow!

[MARY *goes out* U C, *her hand held to her posterior.* ELIZABETH *crosses back and sits as before.*]

JANE. Would you care for a cup of tea, Mama?

MRS. BENNET [*insulted*]. Tea—when my heart is broken? Oh, to think that your father would leave London without finding a trace of them!

JANE. We must hope for the best.

MRS. BENNET. Who is to fight Wickham and make him marry her now? [*She speaks in her normal tone.*] Tell cook to make the tea strong, with plenty of sugar.

[HILL *comes in* D R *with a tray. On it is a cup of tea.*]

JANE. I have already told her, Mama.

HILL [*as she crosses to the settee*]. It is nice and hot, madam, and will do you good.

[JANE *takes the cup of tea and hands it to* MRS. BENNET.]

MRS. BENNET. It will take more than tea to comfort me now. [*But she immediately begins to sip the tea with evident enjoyment.*]

HILL [*trying to get their attention*]. Ahem!

JANE. What is it, Hill?

HILL. I thought you might like to hear that Netherfield is occupied again.

MRS. BENNET [*pausing with the cup halfway to her lips*]. What?

HILL. So the housekeeper informed me. Mr. Bingley is expected back this morning.

ELIZABETH. Thank you, Hill.

[HILL *goes out* D R.]

MRS. BENNET [*her spirits lifted*]. So—Mr. Bingley is returning!

[JANE *rises, walks* U C, *turns to* R *stage, and stands with her back to the others, agitated.*]

MRS. BENNET. Did you hear that, Jane? Not that I care about it, though. He is nothing to us, and I'm sure *I* never want to see him again.

ELIZABETH [*firmly*]. Your tea is getting cold, Mama.

MRS. BENNET. However, he is very welcome to come to Nether-field if he likes. And who knows *what* may happen?

ELIZABETH. Perhaps the tea isn't sweet enough. [*She rises.*] Shall I ring for Hill?

MRS. BENNET. Of course, we agreed long ago never to mention his name. [*She inquires suddenly.*] Is it quite certain he is coming?

JANE [*turning and speaking with spirit*]. Surely Mr. Bingley can return to his house without all this speculation!

MRS. BENNET. As soon as he arrives, my dear, your father must wait on hiim.

JANE [*crossing to* C *stage*]. Papa shall do nothing of the kind.

ELIZABETH. Should we not leave the initiative to Mr. Bingley?

MRS. BENNET. What ungrateful daughters I have! Was ever a poor mother more put upon! [*She cries anew.*]

[MRS. BENNET *rises.* ELIZABETH *quickly takes the cup of tea from her and places it on the mantel, along with her needle-work.*]

MRS. BENNET. All this excitement has been too much for my poor strength!

[ELIZABETH *takes* MRS. BENNET'S *arm.*]

JANE. I'm sorry to distress you, Mama, but I will not allow myself to be forced upon Mr. Bingley again. If he wants my society, let him seek it.

ELIZABETH [*to* MRS. BENNET]. Shall I help you to your room?

MRS. BENNET [*whimpering*]. Don't bother. [*She pulls away and starts* D R.] I must bear all my sufferings—*alone!*

[MRS. BENNET *walks slowly out* D R.]

JANE [*after she has gone*]. Lizzy, I assure you the news does not affect me with either pleasure or pain.

ELIZABETH [*moving over to the fireplace*]. I'm sorry that he comes at all.

JANE [*crossing to her*]. I can hardly bear to hear him perpetually talked about. Mama means well, but she doesn't know—— [*Her voice breaks, and then she turns away.*]—no one can know——

[ELIZABETH *puts her arm around* JANE.]

ELIZABETH. I wish I could see some happiness—for both of us.

JANE [*surprised*]. Why, Lizzie, what's wrong?

ELIZABETH [*sitting on the bench*]. I find I can't get him out of my mind for even a moment.

JANE. Mr. Darcy?

ELIZABETH. He no longer cares for me, and I don't know if I love or hate him more!

JANE [*standing upstage of* ELIZABETH, *with her arm about her shoulders*]. Oh, Lizzy! How unfortunate we all seem to be!

[LYDIA *bursts in* U R. *She is followed by* MR. WICKHAM. *They come to* C. *Neither now nor later does either of them show any embarrassment.*]

LYDIA [*loudly*]. Jane! Lizzy! Congratulate me! I'm married!

[JANE *and* ELIZABETH *look at her in amazement.*]

JANE. Lydia! I——Oh, Lydia! [*She rushes to* LYDIA *and embraces her.*]

MR. WICKHAM [*perfectly at ease*]. Allow me to present Mrs. Wickham. [*He bows.*]

LYDIA [*calling*]. Mama—Papa, everybody, come quick! Here I am!

JANE. We didn't know—Papa went to London, but——

LYDIA. La! It was not to be expected he could find us.

[ELIZABETH *has risen.* MRS. BENNET *comes hurrying in* D R, *followed by* CATHERINE. *After a moment,* MARY *comes in* U C *and* MR. BENNET *comes in* U L. MR. BENNET *moves down to the armchair at* L *stage. The others crowd about* LYDIA *at* C *stage.*]

LYDIA [*embracing* MRS. BENNET]. I'm married, Mama!

MR. WICKHAM [*bowing*]. Your dutiful son-in-law, madam. [*He bows to* MR. BENNET.] And yours, sir.

[MR. BENNET *looks hard at him but says nothing.*]

MRS. BENNET. My dear, dear Lydia! Married at sixteen! [*She takes* LYDIA *by both hands and looks at her with pride and admiration.*] And dear Wickham, too. [*She beams at* MR. WICKHAM.]

LYDIA. We were married just a short time ago.

MRS. BENNET [*pulling* LYDIA *down beside her on the settee*]. Your wedding clothes—I must see about them directly. [*She turns to* MR. BENNET.] My dear, you must decide at once just how much you will give her.

LYDIA. Good gracious! When I went away I had no more idea of being married before I came back again! Though I thought it would be very good fun if I was.

MR. BENNET [*coldly*]. I am glad *you* find pleasure in the situation. [*He speaks ominously to* MR. WICKHAM.] Wickham, I would like a word with you.

MR. WICKHAM. Yes, sir.

[MR. BENNET *goes out* U L. MR. WICKHAM *bows, crosses above the settee, and out* U L. MARY *stands right of the settee, while* CATHERINE *is left of it.* JANE *sits in the armchair at* R C. ELIZABETH *sits on the bench again.*]

LYDIA [*gayly*]. Do the people hereabouts know I'm married?

CATHERINE. How can they, when we ourselves have just found out?

LYDIA. I was afraid they might not. We passed Lady Lucas' carriage, and I was determined she should know it. [*She rises and moves to* C.] So I took off my glove and let my hand rest on the side of our carriage—[*She poses with her left hand suspended.*]—so that she might see my ring.

JANE. Lydia—you didn't!

LYDIA. And then I bowed and smiled like anything. [*She bows and smiles to show them.*]

ELIZABETH. Oh, how could you!

CATHERINE [*gazing at it*]. Your bonnet is the prettiest I have ever seen.

MARY [*severely*]. The color is far too gay.

MRS. BENNET [*rising*]. I must tell Hill to prepare the south chamber for our bride and groom. [*She starts* D R.]

CATHERINE [*following*]. I'm going with you. I want to see Hill's face when she hears the news.

MRS. BENNET. Mary, I may find you useful, too.

[*Reluctantly,* MARY *follows* MRS. BENNET *and* CATHERINE *out* D R.]

LYDIA. La! I must tell Mama about my wedding!

JANE. I hope it passed off well.

LYDIA. Aren't you curious to know how it was managed?

ELIZABETH. No!

LYDIA. La! You are both so strange! [*She sits on the settee in an elegant pose.*] But I must tell you how it went off. My uncle and aunt and I went together to the church, and Mr. Wickham and Mr. Darcy met us there.

ELIZABETH [*in amazement*]. Mr. Darcy! [*She rises.*]

LYDIA. Oh, yes! He was the one who found us. La! Was I surprised when he walked in!

JANE. *Mr. Darcy* found you?

LYDIA. Gracious me, he warned me not to say a word about it. But there! The cat's out of the bag—so I may as well go on.

ELIZABETH. What else did Mr. Darcy do?

LYDIA [*airily*]. Oh, he settled dear Wickham's debts here and there—a few thousand pounds or so.

ELIZABETH [*appalled*]. Oh! [*She sits again, on the bench.*]

LYDIA. Then he very kindly settled a thousand pounds on me, and purchased a commission for my dear Wickham in Newcastle.

JANE. Newcastle? You will be living quite far from us.

LYDIA. But you must all come to visit me and I will arrange balls for you. [*She hurries* D R.] I shall ask Mama at once.

[LYDIA *goes out* D R.]

ELIZABETH [*distressed, rising, moving* U L]. That Mr. Darcy should have done all this for our family! The humiliation is almost more than I can bear.

JANE [*gently*]. He has done it for you, Lizzy.

ELIZABETH [*coming behind the settee to* C *stage*]. I'm afraid to let myself believe that.

JANE. You must.

ELIZABETH [*softly*]. I am humble—but I'm proud of him.

[MR. WICKHAM *comes in* U L.]

MR. WICKHAM [*coming down to left of the settee*]. I'm afraid I interrupt sisterly confidences.

ELIZABETH [*coldly*]. You do.

JANE [*politely*]. But it does not follow that the interruption must be unwelcome.

MR. WICKHAM. I should be sorry, indeed, if it were. We were always good friends, and now we are better.

ELIZABETH. I understand you saw something of Mr. Darcy in town?

MR. WICKHAM. I did. [*He continues brazenly, as he moves to in front of the settee.*] He is in good health, and very busy.

ELIZABETH. Perhaps preparing for his marriage with Miss de Bourgh?

MR. WICKHAM. I should not be surprised. His Aunt Catherine has her heart set on announcing *that* engagement.

ELIZABETH. I'm sure I wish him every happiness. [*She moves U C to look out into the garden, as if to dismiss him.*]

[MR. WICKHAM *bows and goes out* D R. ELIZABETH *moves thoughtfully to the fireplace after he leaves.*]

JANE. What Wickham has done in the past is over. Let us try to forget it. [*She rises, moves to the armchair at* L *stage, and sits.*]

[MRS. BENNET, MARY, *and* CATHERINE *come in* D R.]

MRS. BENNET. Now, Mary, sit down and write the items as I tell you.

[MARY *sits at the writing desk at* R *stage and prepares to write.*]

MARY. Yes, Mama.

MRS. BENNET [*standing back of her*]. We must have calico——

CATHERINE [*enviously, sitting glumly in the armchair at* R C]. I wish I were ordering *my* wedding clothes!

MRS. BENNET. Muslin—let me see—and cambric.

[HILL *comes in* U R.]

HILL [*pausing* U R C]. Mr. Charles Bingley, madam.

MRS. BENNET [*flustered*]. Gracious, so soon! Show him in.

HILL. Yes, madam.

[HILL *curtsies and goes out* U R. JANE *is flustered. She rises and looks at* ELIZABETH, *who smiles encouragingly.*]

MRS. BENNET [*moving to* C *stage*]. If you had only put on your new frock, Jane! But you are looking very well. Catherine, stop fretting and greet him with a smile. Mary, Lizzy, your very best manners!

[MARY *and* CATHERINE *rise.* HILL *ushers in* MR. BINGLEY, *and then goes out* U R. MR. BINGLEY *bows* U C, *and the ladies curtsey.*]

MR. BINGLEY. I hope you have no objections, madam, to this early call. [*He crosses down to* MRS. BENNET *at* C *stage.*]

MRS. BENNET. Objections? Dear me, no. None at all. Do sit down, my dear Mr. Bingley. [*She indicates the settee.*]

MR. BINGLEY. Thank you.

[MR. BINGLEY *sits on the settee.* JANE, *about to sit on the left end, changes her mind and goes back hastily to the armchair at* L *stage and sits.* MARY *resumes her seat at the desk, while* CATHERINE *sits in the armchair at* R C. ELIZABETH *sits on the bench* D L.]

MRS. BENNET [*sitting beside* MR. BINGLEY]. It is a long time since you went away.

MR. BINGLEY. Very long.

[MR. BINGLEY *looks at* JANE, *who keeps her eyes downcast.*]

MRS. BENNET. I began to be afraid you would never come back again.

ELIZABETH [*quickly*]. Did you have a pleasant trip from London?

MR. BINGLEY. Very pleasant.

MRS. BENNET. So much has happened since you went away. Miss Lucas is married and settled. And my daughter, Lydia.

MR. BINGLEY. Allow me to offer my congratulations to them both.

MRS. BENNET. Thank you. It's a delightful thing to have a daughter well married. [*She rises.*] Mr. Bingley, you must take family dinner with us very soon.

MR. BINGLEY [*rising*]. I shall be pleased.

[MRS. BENNET *crosses to* C *and motions to the other girls, pointing to the door* D R.]

MARY [*rising, taking the hint*]. I shall finish my notes upstairs, Mama.

MRS. BENNET [*sweetly*]. Certainly, my love.

[MARY *goes out* D R. MRS. BENNET *continues to motion slyly to* CATHERINE *and* ELIZABETH.]

CATHERINE. What is the matter, Mama?

MRS. BENNET [*guiltily*]. Nothing, my dear. [*She continues to motion to her.*]

CATHERINE. But——

MRS. BENNET [*firmly, crossing to her*]. Come, my love, I want to speak to you. [*She takes* CATHERINE *by the arm and leads her* D R.] Lizzy, my dear, I want to speak with you, too.

JANE [*faintly*]. Is it necessary, Mama?

MRS. BENNET. Most necessary.

[ELIZABETH *rises.*]

MRS. BENNET. If Mr. Bingley will excuse us . . .

MR. BINGLEY. I was about to ask if I may have the pleasure of Miss Jane's company for a stroll in the garden?

[MR. BINGLEY *looks at* JANE, *whose eyes are still downcast.*]

MRS. BENNET [*delightedly*]. By all means! [*She speaks firmly.*] Jane!

JANE [*rising*]. Yes, Mama.

[JANE *goes out* U C, *dutifully, followed by* MR. BINGLEY. *As soon as they have gone,* MRS. BENNET *crosses to in front of the settee.*]

MRS. BENNET. I wanted to leave them alone, but this is much better. My dears, he is as fond of her as ever!

ELIZABETH [*crossing to her*]. Mama, I warn you about jumping to conclusions again.

MRS. BENNET. Mark my words, we shall have her at Netherfield yet.

[HILL *comes in* U R.]

HILL. Lady Catherine de Bourgh, madam.

MRS. BENNET. Mercy—Lady Catherine! I can't believe my ears!

ELIZABETH. Show her in.

[HILL *goes out* U R.]

CATHERINE [*who has remained* D R]. She must be calling to see you, Lizzy.

ELIZABETH. That's strange. We thoroughly dislike each other.

[LADY CATHERINE DE BOURGH *sails haughtily into the room from* U R. *She is the dowager type, expensively dressed, formidable, and superior in manner. When she walks she sweeps; when she sits, it is as if she took her place on a throne. She returns the curtseys of the others with a brief nod.*]

LADY CATHERINE [*abruptly, coming to* C *stage*]. I hope you are well, Miss Bennet. [*She glances at* MRS. BENNET.] This lady, I suppose, is your mother?

ELIZABETH. She is.

[MRS. BENNET *curtises again, nervously.*]

LADY CATHERINE [*glancing at* CATHERINE, D R]. And *that*, I suppose, is one of your sisters?

MRS. BENNET [*eager to get into the conversation, moving to her*]. Yes, madam, she is next to my youngest. My youngest is lately married, and my eldest is somewhere about the grounds, walking with a young man, who, I believe, will soon become a part of the family.

LADY CATHERINE [*ignoring her, crossing over in front of the settee, and speaking to* ELIZABETH]. Miss Bennet, I desire to speak with you—*alone*. [*She gives* MRS. BENNET *a look.*]

ELIZABETH. Very well, Lady Catherine.

MRS. BENNET [*fluttering*]. Of course. If there is anything I can do——

LADY CATHERINE [*firmly, not even glancing at her*]. Alone! [*She sits on the settee.*]

MRS. BENNET. Oh, yes, yes! Come, Kitty.

[MRS. BENNET *hurries* D R, *and she and* CATHERINE *go out* D R. ELIZABETH *remains standing near the fireplace.*]

LADY CATHERINE. You understand, of course, Miss Bennet, why I have come here?

ELIZABETH [*astonished*]. Indeed, I do not, madam.

LADY CATHERINE [*in an angry tone*]. However insincere *you* may choose to be, I shall be quite frank. A report of a most alarming nature has reached me.

ELIZABETH. And what has it to do with me?

LADY CATHERINE. It seems that you are scheming to marry my nephew, Mr. Darcy.

ELIZABETH [*astonished*]. Oh! . . . [*She moves back of the settee to* C.]

LADY CATHERINE. Of course, I know that it is a scandalous falsehood. Such an alliance is impossible.

ELIZABETH [*coolly*]. If you believe it impossible, I wonder that you took the trouble of coming so far.

LADY CATHERINE. I insist that you deny the report at once.

ELIZABETH. Indeed!

LADY CATHERINE [*rising*]. *Do* you deny it? Has my nephew made you an offer of marriage?

ELIZABETH. But your ladyship has just said that it was impossible.

LADY CATHERINE [*crossing close to her*]. Miss Bennet, I am Mr. Darcy's nearest relative, and what concerns him, deeply concerns me.

ELIZABETH. But you are no relative of mine—and have no right to bully me into answering your questions.

LADY CATHERINE. Mr. Darcy is engaged to my daughter. [*She moves triumphantly to* L C *and turns*.]

ELIZABETH [*after a momentary pause*]. If that is true, you can have no reason to suppose he will ask me to marry him.

LADY CATHERINE. Impossible girl! [*She sits on the settee again*.] Think twice before you marry one so far above you. My daughter has family, connections, a fortune. You have nothing. Such a marriage would be a disgrace.

ELIZABETH [*crossing to right of the settee and facing her*]. Mr. Darcy is a gentleman. I am a gentleman's daughter. So far, we are equal.

LADY CATHERINE. Tell me, once and for all, are you engaged to him?

ELIZABETH [*firmly, facing front*]. I am not.

LADY CATHERINE. And will you promise me never to enter into such an engagement?

ELIZABETH [*moving* D L]. I will make no such promise.

LADY CATHERINE. This is your final resolve? Very well! [*She rises.*] I shall know how to act. Do not imagine, Miss Bennet, that your ambition in regard to Mr. Darcy will ever be gratified.

[MR. DARCY *has appeared in the doorway* U C *on this last speech. He moves angrily to* C *stage.*]

MR. DARCY. Aunt Catherine! Since Miss Elizabeth is too polite to ask you to leave her house, *I* must ask you to go.

[LADY CATHERINE *turns to him in surprise.*]

LADY CATHERINE. My dear Darcy, if you had listened to the pretensions of this upstart girl——

MR. DARCY. At once!

[MR. DARCY *and* LADY CATHERINE *look at each other. Her eyes fall first. She moves past* MR. DARCY *to* U R C. *She turns to speak to* ELIZABETH.]

LADY CATHERINE. I take no leave of you, Miss Bennet. I send no compliments to your mother. You deserve no such attentions.

[LADY CATHERINE *stalks out* U R.]

ELIZABETH [*distressed, sinking down on the bench*]. Oh, Mr. Darcy, that you should have come upon such a scene!

MR. DARCY [*crossing to her*]. It gives me courage to hope there may still be a chance for me. Is there, Miss Elizabeth?

ELIZABETH [*embarrassed*]. You have done so much for me—for my family. Lydia told me.

MR. DARCY. I asked her not to mention it. In a way, I'm to blame for not having told you of Wickham's true character.

ELIZABETH. *I* wouldn't let you tell *me* anything. It was you who sent Mr. Bingley back here, wasn't it?

MR. DARCY. I was wrong to take him away. Believe me, I hadn't realized the strength of Jane's attachment for him, and of his for her.

ELIZABETH [*rising, moving toward the settee*]. My behavior to you has been unpardonable from the very beginning, and you have repaid it only with kindness.

MR. DARCY. It is *my* behavior that was unpardonable—my abominable pride! [*He follows her.*]

ELIZABETH. And my abominable prejudice! When I think of the things I said to you, I despise myself! [*She sinks down on the settee.*]

MR. DARCY. Am I still the last man in the world whom you could ever be prevailed upon to marry, Miss Elizabeth?

ELIZABETH [*contritely*]. How you must hate me!

MR. DARCY. Is there no possible way in which I can tempt you to accept me?

ELIZABETH. Please, don't! I'm wretched.

MR. DARCY [*taking her hands and drawing her to her feet*]. Beautifully wretched. Elizabeth, I love you.

ELIZABETH. Oh, Mr. Darcy! [*She lowers her head.*]

MR. DARCY [*humbly*]. Will you do me the great honor of becoming my wife?

ELIZABETH [*in a low voice*]. Yes, Mr. Darcy. [*He continues to hold her hand, looking down at her.*] My father—if you wish to ask him—is in the library. [*She nods toward the door U L.*]

MR. DARCY. I shall ask him at once.

[MR. DARCY *puts her hand to his lips and goes out* U L. ELIZA-BETH *stands looking after him, a happy smile on her face, as* JANE *and* MR. BINGLEY *come in* U C.]

JANE [*hurrying to her*]. Lizzy, my dear! I'm so happy! [*She embraces her.*]

[MR. BINGLEY *crosses down to* C, *smiling broadly.* ELIZABETH *looks from one to the other. They are beaming with joy.*]

ELIZABETH. Can I guess the reason? [*She crosses to* C *with* JANE.]

MR. BINGLEY. Miss Jane has promised to become my wife!

JANE [*demurely*]. You will find Papa in the library. [*She nods* U L.]

[MR. BINGLEY *bows and hurries out* U L. JANE *and* ELIZABETH *watch him go, eagerly.* MRS. BENNET *comes in* D R. JANE *rushes to her.*]

JANE. Mama! I'm going to marry Mr. Bingley.

MRS. BENNET [*hugging her*]. Oh, my dear, dear Jane! I'm sure I shan't get a wink of sleep all night. He is the handsomest young man I have ever seen, and you have always been my favorite daughter!

JANE. He believed I was indifferent to him. That's why he left Netherfield so suddenly.

ELIZABETH [*lightly*]. That will teach you not to be so modest, Jane.

JANE. Oh, it's far too much! Why isn't everybody as happy!

[MR. BENNET *comes in* U L. *With him are* MR. BINGLEY *and* MR. DARCY.]

MR. BENNET. My dear, your future sons-in-law!

[MR. BENNET *comes* D L *with* MR. BINGLEY *and* MR. DARCY. *He indicates the two young men, who bow.*]

MRS. BENNET [*astounded*]. Mr. Darcy, *too!*

ELIZABETH [*modestly*]. Yes, Mama. I have loved him for a long time.

JANE [*delightedly*]. Lizzy, dear! [*She rushes to* ELIZABETH *and hugs her.*]

MRS. BENNET [*overcome*]. Good gracious! Lord bless me! Only think! Dear me! Mr. Darcy! Who would have thought it! Oh, my sweetest Lizzy! [*She rushes to* ELIZABETH *and hugs her, too.*] My favorite daughter!

ELIZABETH. Thank you for your good wishes, Mama.

[MR. BINGLEY *crosses to* C *and offers his arm to* JANE.]

MR. BINGLEY. You will excuse us if we walk in the garden?

MR. DARCY [*crossing and taking* ELIZABETH'S *arm*]. Yes. [*He smiles at* ELIZABETH.]

MRS. BENNET. Oh, dear, yes, of course! We will excuse them, won't we, Mr. Bennet?

MR. BENNET [*dryly*]. I think we had better.

[*The two couples go out* U C. MRS. BENNET *stands at* R C, *looking after them, rapturously.*]

MRS. BENNET. Only think of it, I am to have three sons-in-law! [*She moves to the settee and sits.*]

MR. BENNET. If any young men come for Mary or Kitty, send them in. I am quite at leisure. [*He starts* U L.]

MRS. BENNET [*looking front*]. Mr. Bingley, with four or five thousand a year.

[MRS. BENNET *does not notice* MR. BENNET'S *retreat toward the library* U L. *As she continues,* MR. BENNET *goes out* U L.]

MRS. BENNET [*exclaiming*]. And my dear Lizzy! A house in town! And *ten* thousand a year! [*She turns and sees that* MR. BENNET *is missing.*] Mr. Bennet—where are you? [*She hurries toward the door* U L, *still exclaiming.*] Mr. Bennet—

did you hear? [*She goes out* U L, *still exclaiming.*] *Ten* thousand a year—Mr. Bennet! . . .

[*The curtain comes down as she is heard still exclaiming off* U L.]

CURTAIN

WHAT PEOPLE ARE SAYING about *Pride and Prejudice*...

"An outstanding venue for a large, talented female cast and several 'starring' roles for a real showcase. The best of the novel, providing delightful entertainment for an audience. Everyone who read the script fell in love with the story and characters."

J. Allen, Fredericktown High School,
Fredericktown, Ohio

"*Pride and Prejudice* is a faithful condensation of Jane Austen's comedy of manners. Amusing and quirky characters, a charming and comical story with a single interior set make this classic easy and fun to produce. A frothy delight!"   *Michael Self,*
Annie Wright School, Tacoma, Wash.

"The play was incredible. Everyone who saw *Pride and Prejudice* laughed at Lydia and Catherine and cried with Jane and Elizabeth. It was different and exciting not only for those in the cast, but also for those who were part of the audience."

Teri Evans, Lakeland Christian School, Lakeland, Fla.

"This play is very well written. It brings out the humor of this timeless tale and gives depth to the characters even in such a short amount of space."   *Natalie Skutlin,*
New Covenant Christian School, Lebanon, Pa.

"Very nice adaptation of Jane Austen's classic. Appropriate for advanced high school groups or better."   *Katherine Alexander,*
Berkmar High School, Lilburn, Ga.

"*Pride and Prejudice* is a wonderful story/play. It has a wide variety of great characters—it gave my students a chance to stretch as actors. The audience truly enjoyed it."   *Pam Krage,*
Freedom Farm Christian School, Pittsford, Mich.

"This script excellently condenses the main points of the story for the stage. Our cast had a great time and the play was well received by our audience. A fun retelling of the classic story with simple sets—very easy to produce!"   *Nilorie Gabrell,*
Covenant Christian Academy, Loganville, Ga.

"This was a hugely entertaining play, ideal for young people and challenging too. The single set made life much easier!"
Jenny Caley, Cottingham Little Youth Theatre,
East Yorkshire, UK

DIRECTOR'S NOTES

DIRECTOR'S NOTES

DIRECTOR'S NOTES